Dear Reader,

The holiday season is upon us again, and all of us here at the Reader Service would like to extend our warmest wishes to you and your family during this festive time and into the new year.

Our editors have selected this special story as a Christmas gift for our Reader Service members. It's our Christmas present to you!

We hope you enjoy reading this story, as much as we enjoy giving it to you. Have a very merry Christmas and a prosperous New Year.

Seasons Greetings,

Rose Hilliard

Diana Palmer

THE HUMBUG MAN

Silhouette Books

Published by Silhouette Books
America's Publisher of Contemporary Romance

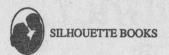 SILHOUETTE BOOKS

ISBN 0-373-15273-6

THE HUMBUG MAN

Copyright © 1986 by Diana Palmer
Originally published in Silhouette Christmas Stories
Copyright © 1986 by Silhouette Books

This edition published by arrangement with Harlequin Enterprises B.V.

® and TM are trademarks of Harlequin Enterprises B.V., used under license. Trademarks indicated with ® are registered in the United States Patent and Trademark Office, the Canadian Trade Marks Office and in other countries.

Printed in U.S.A.

Chapter One

Tate Hollister lived alone, which wasn't surprising to his nearest neighbor. He had a temper like black lightning and seemed to hate people in general, and boys in particular. Maggie Jeffries had gotten an earful about the taciturn rancher from her late father-in-law, and her son Blake was an ongoing verbal documentary on his life. If she hadn't loved the boy so much, she might have had some terrible fights with him over the incredible case of hero worship he had for Hollister. Maggie had seen their black-eyed neighbor from time to time over the years, but he avoided her the same way he tried to avoid Blake. But he didn't have a lot of success with the boy; Blake was almost ten and Hollister was his hero.

It was hard to overlook Blake's constant chatter about the man, but Maggie loved her son, so she tried not to be annoyed. She also kept in mind that Blake had never known his father. Bob Jeffries had been a war correspondent. He'd died in Central America covering a story, leaving Maggie destitute and three months pregnant. She'd supported herself by working as a secretary to a printing corporation executive. When the company had moved its headquarters from Tennessee to Tucson, Arizona, Maggie had decided to go along with little Blake. Her parents were dead and her three brothers were scattered all over the country, but Grandpa Jeffries had still been alive. She wanted to be close enough that Blake could spend some time with him on his rural Montana ranch.

Over the years, Maggie had rapidly climbed to executive secretary and held a responsible job. Then Grandfather Jeffries had died unexpectedly in the fall and had left this small ranch to Maggie.

Blake, who'd been in military school for the past year, had jumped at the chance to go to Montana. Couldn't they, he pleaded, just for the Christmas holidays? Then Maggie could decide if she wanted to sell the place, couldn't she? After all—he played his trump card with a dejected expression that was only partially faked—they hardly saw each other anymore.

That had done it. Maggie missed her son, despite the fact that she wanted him to be independent and not tied to her apron strings. She'd asked for two weeks leave from her job, just through the Christmas and New Year's holidays. Then she'd found them a temporary secretary to take her place, and she and young Blake had left for the wilds of Montana.

And here they were. In two feet of drifting snow, on a rickety, run-down ranch facing the Bitterroot mountains, with no close neighbors except for the elusive and unfriendly Mr. Hollister, whom Blake seemed to worship from afar for God alone knew what reason.

The ranch house was more of a large cabin than a house, but it wasn't uncomfortable. It had just four rooms, two of which were bedrooms. The living room and dining room were combined, with a small kitchen in one corner and a bathroom that was definitely an afterthought. The furnishings were wood, and all of it had a definite Indian influence, from the blankets and rugs to the paintings that decorated the rough wood walls. The only difference now was the few Christmas decorations that Maggie and Blake had added, like the pine boughs around the fireplace with their red velvet bows and the cheerful red and green candles and the artificial holly on the coffee table.

Maggie found the idle pace of life in Montana familiar. It brought back memories of her childhood spent in the mountains of southern Tennessee, so close to the Georgia line that it had once been disputed border territory. She'd lived in the backwoods with her parents and her brothers, and it had been a satisfying life until Bob had passed through covering a story and had wooed Maggie out of her mountains and into Memphis and a small apartment.

Sometimes that part of her life seemed like a long-ago dream. If it hadn't been for the photos, she would hardly remember what Bob looked like, although she'd loved him desperately at the age of eighteen. Now she was twenty-eight, and there were faint threads of silver in her wavy, dark brown hair. She was tall and slender as a willow, but her eyes had a haunted look these days. She was restless lately, and sometimes she felt like she was searching—but she didn't know for what.

"It's fun here." Blake was grinning as he stared out the window at the snow. "I don't miss prickly pear cactus and creosote and roadrunners and dry washes, you bet."

"At least in southern Arizona we didn't have all that snow, or haven't you glanced out the window lately?" she asked, smiling, and her eyes crinkled at the corners. She had an elfin face, very mischievous, and an elegant carriage, which had come from her mother's insistence on proper posture. Those contradictions, added to the faint traces of her southern mountain drawl, made her something of an enigma. She did attract men occasionally, but her rigid Scotch-Irish upbringing didn't allow for a casual outlook on life, and most of the city men she ran across were as easygoing about sex as they were about letting a woman buy them a meal. It was a kind of life that suited many, but Maggie had too many hang-ups. So she was still single.

She wondered sometimes if Blake was being deprived of male companionship solely because of her attitudes. It bothered her, but she didn't want to change.

"Snow is awesome," he sighed, using a word that he used to denote only the best things in his life. Cherry pie was awesome. So was baseball, if the Atlanta Braves were playing, and football if the Dallas Cowboys were.

She smiled at his dark head, so like her own. He had her slender build, too, but he had his father's green eyes. Bob had been a handsome man. Handsome and far too brave for his own good. Dead at twenty-seven, she sighed, and for what?

She folded her arms across her chest, cozy in the oversize red flannel shirt that she wore over well-broken-in jeans. "It's freezing, that's what it is," she informed her offspring. "And it isn't awesome; it's irritating. Apparently, the electric generator goes out every other day, and the only man who can fix it stays drunk."

"That cowboy seems to know how," Blake said hesitantly.

Maggie agreed reluctantly. "I know. Things were running great until our foreman asked for time off to spend Christmas with his wife's family in Pennsylvania. That leaves me in charge, and what do I know about running a ranch?" she moaned. "I grew up on a small farm, but I don't know beans about how to manage this kind of place, and the men realize it. I suppose they don't have any confidence in working for a secretary, even just temporarily."

"Well, there's always Mr. Hollister," Blake said with pursed lips and a wicked grin.

She glared at him. "Mr. Hollister hates me. He hates you, too, in fact, but you don't seem to let that stand in the way of your admiration for the man." She threw up her hands, off on her favorite subject again. "For heaven's sake, he's a cross between a bear and a moose! He never comes off his mountain except when he wants to cuss somebody out or raise hell!"

"He's lonely," Blake pointed out. "He lives all by himself. It's hard going, I'll bet, and he has to eat his own cooking." He sat up enthusiastically, his thick hair over his brow. "Grandpa said he once knew a man who quit working for Mr. Hollister just because the cook got sick and Mr. Hollister had to feed the men."

Maggie glanced at her son with a wicked gleam in her eyes. "He probably fed them some of his razor blades," she murmured.

"Oh, shame on you," Blake said with a chuckle. "How did I wind up with a mother like this?" he asked the ceiling.

"Well, they ran out of ugly, mean ones, and here I was," Maggie sighed, striking a pose.

Blake laughed harder. He would have agreed with her if he could have stopped laughing. He thought she was the best mom in the whole world, even if she did have this annoying hang-up about his beloved Mr. Hollister. "But really, Mom, you're going to have to do something about the cattle and the men pretty quick," he finally said, sounding grown-up and almost knowledgeable. "The cattle are straying real bad. I saw some down on Mr. Hollister's place just this morning."

She drew in a breath. "Why didn't you say so? For God's sake, don't just sit there. Get some barbed wire, and I'll send for a few land mines...." She shuddered.

"He's a nice man. You just don't understand him," Blake said.

She lifted her eyebrows. "Are we talking about the same Mr. Hollister? The one who looks like a hat and mustache sitting on a rock?" she asked, turning away from Blake's amused grin. "I'll bet if he ever smiled, his face would break."

"Grandpa liked him," he reminded her. "I do, too. You just don't know him, that's all. He's a real jake guy."

"I don't want to know him. That's why I spent every minute I came up here hiding out from him. And I will never learn to understand the language you speak," she informed him. "It goes from mumble to street jive to unintelligible—" A loud knock at the door stopped her in midsentence. "Maybe it's the man who can fix the generator," she said hopefully and went to open the heavy oak door.

A rush of cold air hit her in the face, temporarily blinding her. Montana in winter was uncomfortable, even for natives. The windchill factor was nearly unbearable, and the snow never seemed to stop. This small ranch that she'd inherited from her father-in-law was located between the Bitterroot mountain range on the west and the Pryor mountains on the east, with the Wyoming border to the south. Tate Hollister's much larger ranch and enormous house were on her north border and only about a quarter of a mile from the small frame house she shared with Blake.

She wasn't really surprised to find Tate Hollister on her doorstep when she got her eyes cleared of snowflakes. He was tall already, but he seemed to have grown two feet since Maggie last saw him. He glared down at her from black eyes in a thin-lipped, deeply tanned face, which was all hard lines and sharp angles. He looked to be in his late thirties, and he was as wild a man as Maggie had ever seen. In his battered black ranch hat and sheepskin jacket, worn jeans and black boots, he looked like an outlaw. He needed a shave and his mustache needed trimming. His thick, shaggy hair was disheveled. Just the sight of him was enough to intimidate most men, much less Maggie.

"Yes?" she asked with forced pleasantness, her head cocked warily as he removed his gloves and slapped them into his palm.

"Ten head of your cattle are grazing on my winter feed supply," he said without preamble. "What are you going to do about it?"

"Award them the Croix de Guerre for bravery above and beyond the call of duty," she answered without hesitation.

He stared at her as if he wasn't quite certain that he'd heard her. His head tilted slightly and his dark eyes narrowed, while Blake struggled with suppressed laughter. "I don't think you understand the situation," he tried again. "If you don't get them off my land and out of my hay, I'm going to throw down on them."

"That is an old Western expression," Maggie explained to Blake. "It means he's going to shoot them." She looked back at Tate Hollister. "I hope you plan to give them a sporting chance. They are, after all, unarmed." She smiled vacantly.

Hollister's dark eyes were shadowed with surprise, and his mustache actually twitched, but there was no smile on his lips. "Mrs. Jeffries, this isn't a laughing matter."

"Yes, sir." She curtsied. "What would you like me to do about the cattle?"

He looked as confused as a man could. He glanced at Blake, glowering at the boy's grin, which was quickly erased.

"Oh, for God's sake, where's Jack Randall?" he demanded, his deep voice like a bass fiddle with the wind howling outside the door.

She stared at him. "Jack who?"

"Your foreman, lady!"

She sighed. "Oh, him. He left two days before we got here."

"Left!"

She put a hand to her ear. "Please. I have sensitive ears. Yes, he left. He took his wife back east to visit her people for Christmas."

"Christmas!" he muttered, and Maggie stared at him wide-eyed, waiting for him to come out with a hearty "Bah, Humbug." The sentiment was in his expression, even if he didn't say the words, and she had to stifle a giggle. That made him scowl even more. "Are you really this boy's mother?"

Her eyebrows arched. Just because they'd never spoken to each other before was no reason for him to pretend he didn't know who she was. He'd at least seen her a time or two. "Of course," she said.

"I found her under a cabbage leaf," Blake volunteered with twinkling green eyes.

Hollister wasn't amused and after a moment, returned to the subject. "What about the other men?" he asked.

"They're out doing God knows what." She sighed. "We've only been here three days and I can't get one of them to stand still long enough to listen to anything I say. And the man who fixes the electrical generator is—" she hesitated, eyeing Hollister "—indisposed."

"He's out in the bunkhouse drunk," Blake countered, grinning when she glared at him. "Well, he is. I looked in the window."

"Honest to God, you'll die up here in a week," Hollister muttered, glaring at both of them. "City greenhorns! Why in hell didn't you stay in New Mexico where you belong?"

"Arizona," Maggie corrected. "And we don't really belong there. Blake and I moved there from Tennessee."

"Southerners," Hollister grumbled. "Easterners."

She hated that cold, arrogant black stare. She drew herself up to her full height and still had to tilt her head back to look at him. He made her home state sound like the worst kind of insult. Maggie lifted her chin, and her gray eyes sparkled like flint chips. "Well, let me tell you, Mr. Hollister, if I was back home, I'd have plenty of willing help," she replied. "These men seem to think they're being paid by the tooth fairy, and the only mechanic I've got can't walk unless he's carrying a bottle of beer!"

He didn't even flick an eyelash. "No cowboy in his right mind is going to take orders from a city woman with no savvy about ranching. As for the generator, I can fix that."

He antagonized her as no man in her life ever had. She wanted to tell him what he could do with his offer. Damned bossy so-and-so...!

"Well?" he asked, glaring. "I can't work and shine a light all at once. Get me a flashlight, boy."

Blake didn't hesitate. "Yes, sir!" he said smartly and rushed off to look for one.

"Don't order my son around," Maggie said quietly. "I don't like other people telling him what to do."

"If you didn't, you wouldn't have jailed him in a military school," he returned coldly, shocking her because she hadn't realized he knew so much about Blake.

She caught her breath, but before she could say anything, Blake was back with the flashlight. "I'll come and hold it for you," he offered.

"Your mother can do that," he replied with an arrogant smile. "Or don't you know how?"

Her gray eyes flashed, and it was a good thing she didn't see the expression of unholy glee on Blake's face as all his secret plans for bringing these two together seemed to be coming true.

"I'm an executive secretary for a printing corporation," she informed him with blatant hostility. "I can do a lot more than hold a light."

"Oh, I can see how valuable you'd be in an emergency, with all that specialized knowledge," he agreed and turned to open the door. "Get a coat on."

She absolutely gasped. In all her life, she'd never run into anybody like him. He threw out orders like a drill sergeant. And it didn't help that Blake was sitting there with a book on his lap, looking the picture of a studious, polite boy. She stuck out her tongue at him as she put on her leather jacket, and he grinned like a Cheshire cat.

"I'll get you for this," she mouthed at him and left him giggling on the sofa.

She followed the big man around the house, because he hadn't even bothered to wait for her to trudge through the snow with him. He had the flashlight in one enormous gloved hand. He paused by the housing that protected the generator, then thrust the flashlight at her while he uncovered the apparatus and then studied it silently.

"Hold the light on the damned thing, if you please," he shot at Maggie. "I can't see in the dark."

"My God." She whistled. "And you're actually admitting it?"

He muttered something she was glad she couldn't understand.

She grinned as she leveled the flashlight. Odd how refreshing it was to have a man actively dislike her. Most men seemed to feel obliged to chase her. This one wouldn't chase anybody, she mused. He wasn't a marrying man or a particularly romantic one, and it was really fun to antagonize him. She'd never tried to deliberately upset a man before, but it was wildly exhilarating. She felt alive in a way she hadn't for over ten years. Strange, really, since Hollister was the last man in the world she could feel an attraction for.

Hollister paused and scowled down at the generator. "This damned thing came over with the Ark," he muttered. "I don't understand why your father-in-law didn't replace it."

"He probably liked eating," she remarked, pulling her stocking cap over her ears. Snow was falling again. "He wasn't a wealthy man."

"Could have been," he murmured as he stripped off his gloves to reveal huge but elegant hands, which were long-fingered and darkly tanned—capable hands, with callused ridges on the finger pads. "But he kept putting off things."

"Maybe he thought money would corrupt him," she suggested.

His big shoulders shrugged. "It can." He caught her hand that was holding the light and positioned it where he wanted the beam with no regard for her posture. His hand was warm over her own, and curious little tingles went down her spine until he released his brief hold. "Keep it there," he said absently, scowling under the brim of his hat. "Damn. I hope I can splice that wire. . . ."

He pulled out a pocketknife while Maggie watched with fascination. He was a fixer. Most men were, but this one did it with such style. She studied his profile in the faint radiance of the flashlight, fascinated with its hardness, the uncompromising nature it revealed.

He seemed to feel her intent scrutiny because his head turned. His black eyes caught hers and held them, penetrating, questioning. "Well?" he asked curtly.

"You have an interesting hairline," she improvised. Her voice sounded odd. Probably because lightning was running down her spine from that intent black stare.

He lifted a shaggy eyebrow as if he thought she might need immediate mental counseling. "That's a new one."

"Thanks," she said with a grin. "I thought it up all by myself, too."

He tilted his hat back as he worked with the generator. "What the hell are you and the boy doing up here by yourselves?" he asked suddenly.

It was none of his business, and she almost said so. But she stopped herself in time—it wouldn't do to antagonize a man when he was that close to fixing her generator.

"It's almost Christmas. Blake wanted to spend some time with me," she said finally. "He doesn't really like military school, and I think he's out to convince me that I can run a ranch in the wilds of Montana while he sits on a fence and hero-worships you."

He looked at her with wide, disbelieving eyes. "I beg your pardon?"

"Sorry. It slipped out." She leaned against the wall, holding the light steady.

But he wasn't moving. His dark eyes were fixed on her face. "I said: I beg your pardon, lady."

How in the world could a man make an insult of the word lady, she wondered absently. She shifted. "Blake likes you."

"Well, I'm not much on boys," he returned shortly. "Or city women. Or even neighbors. I live alone and I like my privacy. I don't intend having it invaded by your son."

"That's plain enough," she returned, feeling her temper start to rise. "Now let me tell you something. I don't like men in general and you in particular, and what I think of your type of man would fill a book! As for my son, he's only nine years old and he never knew his father. His grandfather is the only male besides you that he's ever spent any time around. And Papa Jeffries was kind and gentle and loving—the exact opposite of you. Blake doesn't know what a man is, so you'll have to forgive his attachment to you!"

His left eye had narrowed and his jaw was clenched. "You are playing one dangerous game, lady," he said shortly.

"I'm so sorry if I've offended you, Mr. Hollister," she replied coolly. "And I promise you Blake won't be allowed within a mile of you for the entire two weeks we're in residence."

"You won't last two weeks if you don't get this outfit into shape," he said shortly as he looped a wire and stayed it with a screw. "There. Let's try it now."

He replaced the cover and started the generator. Maggie had to concede that Hollister was good with his hands. He was lucky, she thought venomously, that he had something to make up for his lack of looks.

Hollister slid his gloves back on and didn't glance at her. She brought back painful memories, she and her son. It had been six years, but he still grieved for his own family. He didn't want or need complications, but this woman could get under his skin. And that irritated him. She opened his wounds and made them bleed. The boy rubbed salt in them.

Blake opened the door and let them back in. "The heater's running!" He grinned up at the big, unsmiling man. "Thanks, Mr. Hollister. We'd have frozen to death but for you."

Hollister's black eyes went over that boyish face with something less than affection. The boy looked like a boy—all uncombed hair and eyes that sparkled with mischief. Just like his mother. The pair of them were going to give him problems. He could feel it in his bones. He missed the old man, because Jeffries had never bothered him. But Blake had, at every opportunity. When he'd come to visit Jeffries for the summer, Tate couldn't walk for bumping into him. It had been irritating at first, and then frankly painful. He'd been glad when the boy left at the end of summer and went back to school. Now here he was back again, and Hollister was feeling the same old stabs of memory, only they were worse. Because now she was here, too, and he'd been a hell of a long time without a woman. She aroused sensations that he'd forgotten he could feel, and he hated them. Damn it, he hated the world . . . !

Maggie glanced at him, surprised by his cold reaction to Blake's gratitude. He was a cold man, though, she thought as she got out of her cap and jacket and boots. Thank God he wasn't going to be around very much.

"Yes, thank you for fixing the generator," Maggie agreed. "I suppose you need to get home, so I won't offer to make coffee. . . ."

She didn't want to, she meant. Oddly enough, that irritated Hollister. He didn't like the way she reacted to him. He knew he wasn't pretty, for God's sake, but did she have to make it so obvious that she found him ugly?

"Those cattle have got to be moved. I'll find your men and set them to it."

"Thank you," she said, deciding against arguing because it would only keep him here longer, and she didn't want that.

"Wouldn't you like a cup of coffee?" Blake invited, while Maggie felt herself choking. No, Blake, she moaned inwardly.

Hollister saw that look in her eyes and just for the hell of it, he said yes.

Maggie forced a smile to her lips. Be generous, she told herself. He fixed the generator. You won't freeze. The least you can do is give the poor cold man a cup of hot coffee. If only she could have managed to get him in the pot with it. . . .

"What do you take in your coffee, Mr. Hollister?" she asked with forced sweetness.

He took off his hat, revealing his thick black hair. Snow flaked from the hat as he placed it on the hat rack and shed his thick coat. Under it he was wearing a red flannel plaid shirt and as near as she could tell, no undershirt. The flannel was unbuttoned halfway down his brawny dark chest, and it had the thickest covering of hair she'd ever seen on a man.

She stared at him. She couldn't help it. Despite her very brief marriage, she knew almost nothing about men. Bob had been as inexperienced as she, and as shy, so she'd learned little during those few fumbling encounters in the dark. But Hollister had a savage masculinity, an untamed look that made her blood run crazy and her pulse do unexpected things. She didn't even like him, but he had a dangerously sensual appeal. She forced her eyes back to the white mugs she was pouring coffee into.

"I take my coffee black, Mrs. Jeffries," Hollister said quietly.

She'd known that somehow before she'd posed the question. He looked that kind of man. No frills, no embellishments. She'd have bet that he drank his whiskey straight and never put catsup on his meat. She looked up as he came close to take the cup, smelling of wind and fir trees and leather.

"I'll bet you never put catsup on a steak," she said without thinking.

He searched her eyes curiously. "As a matter of fact, I don't," he agreed. His heavy brows moved together faintly. "What brought that on?"

She dropped her eyes to her coffee. "I don't know." She lifted it, even though it was hot. Involuntarily her gaze went to Hollister's hands. They fascinated her, now that she knew how capable they were. They were huge. Lean. Darkly tanned, with thick hair on the wrists and hard muscle in the long fingers. Flat nails, very clean. She could imagine those hands doing anything that was necessary on a ranch, from fixing generators to helping a calf be born.

"Do you still have that big Aberdeen Angus bull, Mr. Hollister?" Blake asked. He'd joined them at the table and was sipping a cola from a can he'd gotten out of the refrigerator.

Hollister hated having the boy ask him questions. But the youngster had a natural feel for ranching, and he remembered vividly the ease with which Blake had helped old man Jeffries deliver a calf and doctor one of the bulls. "I've still got him," he replied tersely. He glanced at Blake, his eyes suddenly curious, losing their sharp edge as he realized that the boy was really interested and not just asking inane questions. "And I've bought a new Hereford crossbreed bull as well. I'm doing a three-one cross this next year. Angus to Beefmaster, Beefmaster to Hereford, and back to Angus again."

"Angus are easy calvers," Blake said knowledgeably. "And Herefords are hardy. And Beefmasters are good choice grade beef."

"With good weight gains ratios," Hollister agreed. The boy had been putting in some study to learn all that. He was impressed despite himself. "I had to sell my Brangus bulls. After two years of inbreeding, you can create some problems for yourself if you don't introduce some new blood into your herd."

"That's a fact," Blake said, sipping his cola.

Maggie, lost, glared at both of them. Hollister happened to glance her way and lifted an eyebrow. He came as close to smiling then as he had in six long years. "Something bothering you, Mrs. Jeffries?" he asked in his deep, slow tone.

"She doesn't know a lot about cattle," Blake said. "But she's a whiz at math and accounts payable and organizing things. She's the top secretary at Skyline Printing Services and a computer expert."

Maggie shifted restlessly. "Don't brag about me that way," she told her son. "I only learned accounting to get out of typesetting. And I learned computer programming to get out of accounting."

"Most women aren't good at math." Hollister's dark eyes narrowed in his hard face. "My mother could barely count hens."

"It was always my best subject in school," Maggie replied. "My dad was a farmer. He kept a tally book, and I was his payroll clerk. He taught me to add columns of figures in my head."

"Her parents are dead now," Blake volunteered. "I have three uncles, but they're spread all over the country and I never see them."

"A farmer?" Hollister persisted. "What kind of livestock did he have?"

"Cattle and hogs," she answered. "He had some high pastures, too. Right on the side of the hills, but he did very well. We had Jersey cows and a few Holsteins."

The tall man finished his coffee. "But you don't know how to breed cattle?"

"A handful of cows, mostly milk cows, doesn't qualify anyone to handle several hundred head of beef cattle," she reminded him. "It's a totally different proposition. And I was only eighteen when I married Blake's father and left the country for the city. I've forgotten most of what little I knew about the management of it."

Hollister's big hands toyed with the empty cup. "I went to school with Bob Jeffries," he said. "He was a grade behind me."

She sat very still. "He died in Central America before Blake was born. We'd been married less than six months." She sighed. "It seems like a dream sometimes. Except for the talking proof sitting there trying to look invisible while he drinks his soda," she added with a dry grin at Blake.

Blake just grinned back, but he was listening.

"Bob loved danger," Maggie reminisced, aware of Hollister's narrow gaze on her face. "He fed on adrenaline. Just after we were married he tried to give it up." She smiled sadly. "It didn't work out. For him it was like trying not to breathe."

"I never knew him," Blake sighed. He looked up at Hollister. "You aren't married, are you, Mr. Hollister?"

Hollister stared into the empty coffee cup. "I was." He put the cup down on the table and turned. "Thanks for the coffee. I'll round up your hands and point them in the right direction." He put on his coat and cocked his hat over one eye, glancing back at Blake and his mother without smiling. "If I were you, I'd stay inside until this snow lets up. And I'll have that fence fixed before I let your men come home."

"Thanks for fixing the generator," she said, alternately relieved and irritated by his shouldering of her own problems.

He opened the door. "No problem. Good night."

He was gone in a whirl of wind and snowflakes, and Maggie stared after him feeling oddly empty and alone. How strange to feel that way about a man she disliked.

"He must be divorced," Maggie said absently.

Blake joined her in the kitchen, draining his can of soft drink. "No, he's a widower," he told her. "Grandpa said his whole family was killed in an accident in the Rockies. Mr. Hollister was driving. His wife and son died, and he didn't." He shrugged, oblivious to the shock and horror on his mother's soft face. "Grandpa said that was why he lived like he does, alone and away from everybody. That he was punishing himself because he didn't die, too. Too bad. He sure is a nice man.''

He glanced at his mother and did a double take at the look on her face. She actually looked interested. And that made him smile, but he was careful not to let her see him doing it.

Chapter Two

With the electrical generator fixed and the snow diminishing, thank God, Maggie spent a day going over the ranch's financial statement. Blake busied himself with a new computer game while listening to Christmas music on a local country and western radio station. She wondered how Grandfather Jeffries had ever made a go of ranching in the first place, having spent so much on adding new land to his ranch when interest rates were sky-high and spending so little on herd improvement.

What little she'd gleaned from Hollister about crossbreeding had piqued her curiosity. She wondered if her father-in-law had been trying that angle, or if he'd just raised beef without worrying about bloodlines or grades at auction.

The really big problem, though, wasn't what the ranch's past had been. It was what its future was going to be. She hated to sell it. There was something majestic and real about rural Montana. About mountains that touched heaven and trees almost that tall. There was space here, not unlike the Arizona she'd come to love, and there were basic values. Blake would love staying on the ranch, having cattle to raise, and he'd have a heritage to inherit. But how was she going to keep it solvent all by herself? As she'd admitted, she knew nothing about the daily routine of ranching, even about how to breed cattle. The worst thing in the world would be to tackle it without expertise. She'd fall flat on her face and lose everything, and where would she be then?

Blake, noting the lines of worry on her oval face, saved the game he'd been playing and, carefully removing the disks first, cut off the computer. He lowered the volume on the radio and turned to face her.

"Something's wrong, isn't it?" he asked.

She smiled. "I'm no rancher," she sighed. "That about sizes it up. This place needs a cattleman, not a vacationing secretary."

"There's always—"

"Mr. Hollister," she bit off with a glittering stare in his direction. "Don't you know any other words?"

Blake grinned, not at all chastened. "His first name is Tate."

She rolled her eyes toward the ceiling and went back to the figures. "I'll never be able to make it work."

"We have a great foreman," Blake said sensibly. "And that's mainly all we need."

"You make it sound so easy," she replied and smiled wearily at him. Probably at his age everything was easy. It was only when people grew up that life got so complicated. "Well, I'll think about it," she promised.

But Blake went to bed that night frowning because she'd had that look on her face. The one that said: I'm quitting while I'm ahead. And at all costs, he couldn't possibly let her out of these mountains before he got a good chance to bring her and Mr. Hollister together. They were both alone, about the right age, and he doted on them. Why wouldn't it work? He turned off his light so his mother would think he was sleeping, and before he dropped off to sleep he had the answer.

Maggie made pancakes the next morning, and Blake ate two helpings before he got up from the table, put on his boots and thick parka and announced that he was going to hike down the ridge to the river and see if it was frozen.

"You be careful," she cautioned as he went out, reminding herself that young boys had to have some independence and that she couldn't keep him indoors for the rest of his life.

"Sure I will," he promised. He chuckled. "See you in a couple of hours. I've got my watch on, so I'll know when I'm due back, okay?"

She smiled gently. "Okay."

But two hours passed, joined by two more, and still he didn't return. Maggie was frantic. She tried searching, but she didn't have any idea how to find which way he'd gone. She didn't trust the men, either. Not with Blake's life. She grimaced and gritted her teeth and tried to stay calm. There was only one person in the world she did trust to find Blake. In a fever of impatience, she got into the four-wheel-drive Bronco that Blake had talked her into buying in the summer and went quickly down the road to the Hollister place.

The Hollister house was a big rugged retreat, with a varnished wood exterior, all angles and glass. Every possible view had its own window, and judging by the number and size of the chimneys, it must have as many fireplaces. Maggie had never set foot inside it, but she'd seen it often enough from the road.

She jumped out of the Bronco, tugging her leather jacket closer against the biting wind. The windchill in these parts was formidable, even in December.

The front porch was long and rambling, with plenty of chairs, but she didn't stop to admire the view. She knocked frantically at the front door and only then wondered what she was going to do if he wasn't home. What if he was gone for the day, or out on business, or...

The door opened. Tate Hollister eyed her over a cup of steaming coffee, his blue-checked flannel shirt the only bright and welcoming thing about him as he stared down at her.

"I don't recall inviting you to lunch," he said.

She glared at him. "Blake's missing," she said hesitantly. Now that she was here, it was even harder than she'd imagined. He did look like stone, mustache and all.

"Don't look at me," he said imperturbably. "I don't have him."

"He said he'd be gone two hours." She gnawed her lower lip. "He went down to the ridge to see if the river was frozen. That was four hours ago, and it's snowing again." Her soft gray eyes looked up at him helplessly. "I can't even find tracks."

"He's playing a prank," he told her easily. "When he's had enough, he'll come home."

"He's not," she argued. "Blake is like me. If he says he'll do something, he'll do it. He doesn't play pranks."

"You don't know much about boys, do you?" he mused.

She was freezing, and his attitude wasn't warming her at all. "No, I guess I don't," she admitted flatly. "I've been too concerned with trying to support us to have much free time to learn, either, and Blake is a handful sometimes."

His dark eyes went slowly over her face, as if he hadn't really looked at it before. Around them, the wind blew and snow peppered the porch, but he didn't seem to notice.

"He might be hurt," she said with involuntary softness. "I'm afraid."

He pursed his lips, the mustache twitching. "It's a prank," he repeated. "But I'll come. You can wait inside if you like, while I get my coat."

She didn't understand why, but she didn't want to go in that house. She thought suddenly of the wife and child he'd lost, and her feet froze to the porch. It would be like trespassing.

"No," she hesitated. "I'll . . . I'll just wait out here, thanks."

He frowned slightly, puzzled, but he shrugged and went off after his coat.

She was standing by the Bronco when he came out, his torso and lean hips covered by the thick shepherd's coat, his thick black hair under the wide brim of his black Stetson and what looked like a rifle in one hand. At closer inspection, it was, and she frowned.

"You can drive if you like..." she began, but he was going the other way. "Where are you going?" she called, running to keep up with him as he went toward the stables down the road from the house.

"You're crazy if you think I'm taking a vehicle, even with four-wheel drive, down that ravine," he said easily. "I'm going out on horseback."

"With a rifle? What are you going to do with it?"

He spared her an impatient glance. "Oh, for God's sake, woman, I'm not going to shoot the boy."

"I didn't say so," she faltered.

He made a sound that refuted that and kept walking while she ran along behind him.

"You can wait in the house or go home," he said. He opened the stable door, and she saw a wide alley filled with wood chips with bright, clean stalls on either side, some of which housed horses.

"He's my son. I want to come, too."

He turned, staring at her. "Can you ride?"

"Of course I can ride," she said irritably.

"Well, well. You aren't quite the lily I thought you were," he mused as he went to the tack room.

And what did that mean, she wondered, but anxiety kept her quiet. He saddled a quiet little chestnut mare for her and a huge buckskin gelding for himself. Snow was falling steadily as they stood outside the stable.

"Molly won't toss you, but she has a tendency to scrape people off against tree trunks, so keep your eyes open," he said as he held the mare for her to mount.

She swung easily into the saddle, sitting tall, the reins held lightly in her hands.

He looked up. His dark eyes approved her excellent posture and he smiled. It was the first time she recalled ever seeing him smile, and his face didn't even break.

"No hat," he said then and went back to the tack room again, returning with a beat-up old Stetson, which came down to her ears but did keep the snow off. "Let's go." He swung into his own saddle and took the lead. "Keep in my tracks," he said over his shoulder. "And don't stray off."

"Yes, sir, Mr. Hollister," she muttered under her breath.

"What was that?"

She averted her eyes from that black stare. "Not a thing."

There might have only been the two of them in the world as they rode out through the tall lodgepole pines and aspens, where the snow was less thick, and Maggie thought irrelevantly that this was the best way to see Montana. Not in a car, or on foot. But on the back of a horse, with leather creaking as they rode, and the smell of the fresh mountain air and the bite of the wind and snow on her face. If she hadn't been so worried about Blake, she might have even been able to appreciate it.

She was still tense, but somehow she knew that whatever was wrong, Hollister would be able to handle it. She glanced at him curiously, wondering at the sense of security she felt with him, even in an emergency like this one. Which brought her mind back to Blake and to the hundred things that might have happened to him, the least of which was enough to make her nauseous. He was all she had . . . !

"I said," Hollister repeated curtly, "which way did he go when he left the house?"

She looked up, to see her own cabin just before them. She had to blink twice to get her mind back on track. "Sorry." She bit her lower lip. "He went there," she nodded toward the back of the cabin, down the long hill behind.

He spared her an irritated glance before he urged his mount forward, so much at home in the saddle that he seemed part of the big buckskin. Halfway down the ridge, he held up his hand and swung down, kneeling in the snow to look. He went on foot from there, stopping to examine limbs, his eyes keen and quick as they darted around the mountainous terrain of the forest.

"He went through there," he murmured, his eyes narrowed as he studied the downward slope. His head went up, and he listened. Maggie heard it, too—a voice.

"Blake!" Hollister's deep tones cut through the wind, carrying, bellowing.

"Hellllp!"

The cry was definitely Blake's, and there was an odd note of fear in it. Maggie almost cried out herself, feeling that piercing cry to her soul.

Hollister didn't spare Maggie a glance. He whipped his rifle out of the sheath on his saddle and swung back up onto the horse, wheeling the animal in the direction of the shout.

Maggie urged her mount after him, terrified. Hollister wasn't a hysterical man. If he reacted that way, there was a reason. But even as she was thinking it, she heard the sound, and it chilled her to the bone. A sob caught in her throat. She knew the howl of coyotes, but this sound was deeper, richer, more threatening. It was the howl of a wolf . . .

Hollister urged his mount down the ridge at a clip Maggie did her best to follow, frustrated that the snow made it such an ordeal to get to Blake.

With her heart hammering in her throat, blind fear choking her, she held on to the reins and felt her heartbeat shaking her as she heard Blake's shrill voice.

Ahead of her, Hollister made his way quickly through another thick stand of aspens, through the thick underbrush, and Maggie, right on the heels of his mount, caught a horrifying glimpse of a small dark head far below, near the ribbon of stream that cut through the snow. Blake! And only a few yards away, stalking, a big silver wolf.

Maggie felt her heart stop. Her son. Her boy! She saw Hollister swing out of the saddle, heard his voice.

"Don't move!" he yelled at Blake and sighted down the rifle barrel with an economy of motion that was as menacing as the wolf itself.

There was a sudden report, and then another and another, the crack of rifle fire echoing with horrible violence down the ridge and up the next slope, at odds with the pastoral beauty and peace it disturbed.

"Blake!" Maggie screamed, tears sliding down her cheeks as she swung out of the saddle. There was smoke from the rifle in Hollister's hands, but even before it cleared, he was down that slope, his big frame absorbing the shock of his steps with grace and ease. Maggie was right behind him.

"Mr. Hollister! Mom!" Blake cried, his voice excited and high-pitched with pain.

Through her tears, Maggie could see the unnatural angle that Blake's left leg was lying at. Broken for sure, she thought sickly, and thanked God for Tate Hollister.

The man knelt quickly beside the boy, the rifle cast aside as he felt the lower leg, and Blake winced. Maggie got on Blake's other side, hugging him, shaking with reaction.

"Broken," Hollister murmured. "A simple fracture, thank God, not a compound one. What happened?"

"Lost my footing." Blake tried to grin. "I came out...to check the river. Gosh, Mr. Hollister, that wolf sure was a beaut. I guess that's why you didn't kill him, huh?"

"Timber wolves are damned near extinct," Hollister said as he got up and broke two limbs off a tree. "If he hadn't turned tail, I wouldn't have had a choice, but I flushed him. I hate killing when I don't have to. Maggie, I need some cloth to make a splint," he said as he pulled a folded blanket from its position just behind the saddle on his horse. He wrapped the limbs to make a cradle and then very carefully drew the cradle under Blake's leg.

It was the first time he'd ever called her by name, and Maggie couldn't understand why her heart ran wild. She let go of Blake long enough to hand him the wool scarf around her neck.

"Will this do?" she asked in a quivering tone, handing the scarf to him while Blake gripped her hand tightly and tried to reassure her that he was all right.

"Hi, guy," she said and spoiled her stiff upper lip by bursting into tears.

"Aw, cut it out, Mom," Blake muttered. "It's just a broken leg."

"Excuse me," she said, trying to laugh. "You know how mothers are."

Hollister glanced at her, but he didn't say anything. He whipped out his pocketknife and made a neat slit right down Blake's boot so that the whole thing was laid bare and easily removed. Then he positioned the sticks he'd broken on either side of Blake's leg and put his wool bandanna next to Maggie's. "OK," he told Blake quietly. "This is going to be rough. I have to straighten that leg and splint it, and it's going to hurt like hell. Want something to bite on?"

"Oh, but you can't—" Maggie was already protesting.

"Shut up," he told her, his eyes black and steady and challenging.

She did, instantly, without an argument, because that hard glare was like a dash of cold water.

"I'll be OK," Blake said through his teeth, nodding. He clenched his hands at his sides and propped himself on them. "Go ahead."

Maggie felt tears spurt from her eyes as Hollister worked, his hands deft and sure. Blake cried out just once and almost blacked out when Hollister pulled the leg straight, but the boy never let out another sound, even while the makeshift splint was put on and tied in place. But his face was as white as plaster when Hollister finished.

"OK?" Hollister asked, and his voice was different. Gentle. Deeper. He smiled at the boy.

Blake beamed. He managed a grin because it was like a turning point in his relationship with the taciturn rancher. "OK," he agreed.

"Here." Hollister handed his rifle to Maggie. "Wait a minute. Let me put the safety on." He did that and handed it back. "Don't shoot yourself in the foot," he cautioned.

She glared at him. "I know which end to point, thanks."

Tate didn't smile, but his dark eyes twinkled. He lifted Blake very carefully, but Blake's breath sucked in at the pain the movement caused. "This is doing it the hard way, I know," he told Blake as he carried him to the buckskin, "but it can't be helped. Back in the old days, the Plains Indians made a travois and pulled injured warriors back to camp on it."

"A . . . travois?"

"That's right." Hollister propped Blake on the saddle while he swung into it behind him and turned him over his knees, wonderfully gentle even though Maggie could see the pain in Blake's young face. "I'll tell you about it on the way back," he said, nodding to Maggie who'd managed to get the rifle back into Hollister's saddle horn before she'd mounted the mare.

She let Hollister take the lead, wondering at his skill as a woodsman as he led them right back up to the cabin with no fuss or side trips, talking softly to Blake the whole time, his deep voice steady and comforting. It dawned on her then that he wasn't just making conversation. He was keeping Blake calm so that he didn't go into shock.

She wondered what she would have done if Tate hadn't been around. She'd have done her best, but would it have been good enough? Just the thought of that wolf made her blood run cold. But the man she'd imagined Hollister to be would have killed the wolf without a second thought. Instead, he'd managed to run it away because he didn't like to kill things unless he had to. Her gray eyes watched his tall form quietly, curiously, and new feelings began to bud inside her.

"Keep him warm," he told Maggie after they'd gotten back to the cabin and he'd put Blake carefully on the sofa. "A couple of aspirin wouldn't come amiss until we can get him into Deer Lodge to the doctor. Keep him talking. It will help him fight off shock. I'll take the horses home and bring the Bronco back as quick as I can. You left the keys in it, right?"

She nodded and started to speak, but he was gone before she could get her mouth open.

"Isn't he something?" Blake sighed through his pain.

"He is that," Maggie agreed. She brushed back his dark hair. "Are you going to make it?"

"Sure," he said, grinning. "I'm tough."

"I guess you are, at that. I'll get those aspirin."

By the time Hollister got back, Blake was in a little less pain, although he was still groaning a little.

"I'll put him on the back seat," Hollister said, lifting Blake gently. "You'd better sit back there with him. The way the snow's coming down, we may slide a bit getting down into the valley."

"I wish I could thank you enough—" she began.

"Get the door," he said tersely, ignoring her efforts to tell him how she felt.

She sighed softly and did what she was told.

All the way to Deer Lodge, holding Blake's head in her lap, she wondered at her new acceptance of Hollister's rough demeanor. He made her feel feminine. Watching the easy, confident way he handled the Bronco, she recalled the same ease with which he'd repaired the generator, handled the emergency of Blake's broken leg, routed the wolf and got them down the mountain in deep snow. He was simply amazing. And she was suddenly hurt that he had a past that wouldn't allow him to lose his heart because it was dawning on her that she wanted it. She wanted to learn everything there was to know about him. She wanted to smooth away the hard lines from that dark face and make him laugh. She wondered if he even knew how to laugh, with all the tragedy he'd known.

Dr. Peters examined Blake's leg at the small clinic and set it, commending Hollister's knowledgeable first aid treatment as he put on a thick plaster cast. He wrote Maggie a prescription for pain pills to give the boy, praised him on his bravery and told him when to come back to have the cast removed.

Maggie didn't even think about it until they'd stopped by the pharmacy to get the prescription and were on the way back up the mountain. They'd be back in Tucson when that cast had to come off. She'd have to be back at work, but how could she possibly send Blake back to military school? She frowned, gnawing her lower lip as the thought of leaving the ranch began to make her feel sick.

"Reaction," Hollister mused, watching her. She was sitting in the passenger seat now, because Blake had a dose of sedative in him and was almost asleep on the back seat. "Don't worry. I wish I had a nickel for every broken bone I've set over the years. He'll be fine."

"What?" she asked quietly.

"Now that it's all over you're going green, Mrs. Jeffries," he murmured dryly. He was smoking a cigarette, the acrid smell of it filling the cab as he easily handled the sliding motion of the Bronco on a patch of hard ice and whipped it around the next horrible curve as they wound back up to the cabin.

"I think I'm entitled," she said gently and smiled at him.

His dark eyes studied that smile, intent on her soft mouth, and his thick eyebrows drew together. "Yes," he said after a minute, dragging his eyes back to the road. "I guess you are."

"Don't you ever smile?" she asked suddenly, the words popping out before she could stop them.

He didn't look at her. "Not often. Not anymore."

She wanted to say more. She wanted to ask him about the accident. She wanted to tell him that he shouldn't live in the past. But she didn't have that right, and she was shocked at her own forwardness. She loved her own privacy. It was odd that she should feel free to infringe on his.

She blushed as she looked out the window at the distant majesty of the mountains all around, blue and white against the gray sky.

"Now what is it?" he asked.

She shifted restlessly. "Nothing."

"You colored."

He saw too much. "I wanted to thank you for what you've done," she said. "You . . . make it difficult."

"I don't want thanks," he said simply. He lifted the cigarette to his chiseled lips. "Up here, we look out for each other. It's how we survive."

"I can't imagine you letting anybody look out for you," she sighed.

He glanced at her with both eyebrows arched.

She shivered, pulling her jacket closer. "Well, I can't," she said doggedly, and her silvery eyes glinted at him.

The mustache twitched, and his dark gaze had a twinkle in it as he turned his attention back to the road. "I'm glad the boy was all right."

"Yes, so am I." She shivered again. "Just thinking about that wolf . . ."

They were at the cabin now. He stopped the Bronco and cut off the engine, turning to look at her. It was almost dark, and in the going light he could see the strain in her face, the worry darkening her eyes. A woman alone with a boy was hard going, especially when she was their only support. He wondered if she'd ever let herself lean on a man since the death of her husband and figured that she probably hadn't.

"He's all right," he reminded her.

"No thanks to me," she laughed huskily and heard her own voice break.

His chin lifted while he studied her. "Come here," he said, catching her arm with his free hand. "Come on," he said when she hesitated. "I guess you need a good cry."

It seemed strange, letting him hold her when they'd been strangers. But he didn't feel like a stranger anymore. He'd saved Blake and taken care of everything, and she felt safer with him than she'd ever felt with anyone. She sighed, giving way to the tears while he held her, one lean hand smoothing her hair, his deep voice quiet and comforting at her temple.

"I'm sorry," she said after a little, embarrassed at her lack of composure. "It frightened me."

"It should have. Don't let the boy wander off like that again," he said, his tone firm and commanding. "This isn't downtown Tucson. There are wolves around here and even a few bears."

"He isn't likely to go far with a broken leg," she reminded him, her gray eyes meeting his.

"No, I guess not." He was looking into those silvery pools and forgot what he was going to say. He couldn't seem to look away. His body tautened and his breathing seemed to go haywire. God, she was pretty! His face hardened. He didn't want or need this . . . !

Maggie was having problems of her own. Her heart was going wild from that look. She felt like a young girl with her first beau. Involuntarily, her eyes dropped to his mouth under the thick black mustache, to the beautifully cut lines of his hard lips, and she wanted to kiss him.

"Oh, no," he said suddenly, and his lean hand contracted in her hair, tugging her face up to his. "No, you don't, lady. I'm not going that route again in one lifetime." He let go of her all at once and opened the door.

Maggie felt nerveless. She didn't understand what he'd said, unless he was insinuating that he'd loved his wife and didn't want to risk his heart twice. She even understood. But she hadn't been trying to tempt him . . . or had she?

She watched him get Blake out of the Bronco and thanked him tersely as he laid the boy on the bed in his room and went back out again.

"I'll bring the Bronco back later, when I get one of my men to ride with me," he said coldly. "Is there anything you need?"

He was as icy as the wind. She wouldn't have asked him for a crumb if she'd been starving. "No, thank you, Mr. Hollister," she said with remarkable calm, considering how churned up she felt. She even managed to smile faintly. "Thank you for all you've done."

He searched her face with eyes that didn't want to see the pain he'd just caused with his remoteness. He turned to the door. "No problem," he said curtly and left without a backward glance.

Chapter Three

Blake rested fairly well that night, thanks to the medicine the doctor had prescribed for him. But Maggie was wakeful and restless. Her mind kept going back to Hollister, to a day that was going to live forever in her memory, like the man who was such a part of it.

She hadn't wanted this complication in her life. For years she'd kept men at a safe distance. She'd dated, but with the careful stipulation that she was searching only for friendship. Once or twice she'd had to ask to be taken home because some of her dates had been quite sophisticated and certain that they had the perfect cure for her reserved attitude about sex. But Maggie wasn't interested in cures or even in men. Her brief marriage had left her unsatisfied and a little embarrassed at her own sexuality. She didn't understand the restlessness she'd been feeling lately or her rather frightening attraction to Tate Hollister. She knew so little about men and intimacy. Far too little to handle a violent emotional upheaval in her life. All she wanted now, she told herself, was her job and her son. Or she had. The trouble was that Tate Hollister was suddenly coloring her world.

It was the longest night in recent memory. She didn't sleep until the wee hours of the morning and woke to freezing cold. Dragging herself out of bed in her blue flannel pajamas, she went to the thermostat and tried to turn on the furnace, only to discover that there was no electricity. Again.

She moaned. Well, wasn't this just the berries, she thought gnashing her teeth. Infuriated, she went to the fireplace, where she'd laid a fire the night before and searched for matches. Then she remembered that she'd used up the last one and hadn't thought to ask Hollister for the loan of a pack. Not that they'd have done much good. She didn't have any wood except what was in the fireplace. Nobody had cut any more.

She sat down on the sofa and burst into tears. Her whole life seemed to be falling apart.

The knock on the door came as a shock. She stared at it, frowning because it was barely dawn. Could it be one of the men? She went to it, hesitating because she was in her pajamas and didn't have a robe handy. She opened the door just a crack and found a familiar hard, mustached face.

Her heart jumped, and the light that came into her face seemed to paralyze the man on the porch for a split second. He studied what he could see of her with a faint twinkle in his own eyes.

"Your generator's down again," he said.

"Yes, I noticed. How did you know?"

"I wanted to see if my jury-rigging was going to hold since the temperature dropped so much last night," he said with a curious inflection that made her suspicious.

"Did you?"

"I can't fix it without the proper supplies, anyway," he said impatiently. "So I guess that being the case, you and Blake had better come home with me until this weather lets up."

Her heart ran away. She had doubts about it, and she wanted to ask more questions about that generator because he did look suspicious. But his dark eyes had found hers, and she couldn't quite look away from them.

"Come . . . home with you?" she faltered.

"Mmm-hmm," he murmured, as oblivious to what they were saying as she was. She was pretty even without makeup, and her gray eyes were oddly welcoming.

"Would you . . . like some coffee?" she asked, without realizing that if she didn't have any power, she certainly couldn't make any.

"Sure," he replied.

She opened the door, moving back, and she flushed scarlet when he came in the door and got a good look at her pajama-clad, barefoot figure.

"Oh," she exclaimed, pausing while she tried to decide what to do.

His dark eyes raked over hers, and there was a faint flush high on his cheekbones.

"I . . . I'd better get something on," she began.

"You better had," he agreed.

But she couldn't seem to convince her legs because they wouldn't move. She stood helplessly, feeling her breasts swell, feeling her heartbeat shaking the low V of the pajama top so that he had to be able to see it. In fact, his eyes had dropped there and narrowed as he looked, and that flush on his cheekbones that was so puzzling got even darker.

Her lips parted. No, it wouldn't work. She was afraid to go with him, afraid of what was happening. "Blake and I . . . had better stay here," she said huskily. "But thanks anyway."

Her breath stopped as he suddenly bent and lifted her in his hard arms, carrying her straight back to her bedroom. His booted heel caught the door and slammed it. He put her down then, slowly, with her back to the door.

"What are you afraid of?" he asked quietly.

She felt the cold door at her back and the even colder floor under her feet, but her body was blazing with sensation as he paused just a foot away. "You," she confessed.

His dark eyes went over her like hands, fascinated, intent. "I guess that should flatter me?"

She moved restlessly under the pressure of his black stare. "You've been married," she said hesitantly. "So have I, but only for a few months, and I haven't dated very much since Blake was born."

That surprised him, although with what he was learning about her, it shouldn't have. He tilted his hat back, watching her face. "No sex?" he asked quietly, not dressing it up.

She blushed scarlet and her eyes dropped. She shook her head.

His lean hand went to her chin, tilting it up, and for all its cool deftness, it didn't insist. "Yes, I was married," he said gently. "To a woman who avoided the very touch of me."

She stopped being afraid and just stared, astonished. "But . . . you had a child."

He sighed heavily. "Most people think that. I've let them think it to prevent gossip for the sake of her people." He touched her hair lightly, as if its dark silkiness fascinated him, while her rapt gaze remained fixed on his hard face. "She was my brother's girl. He was killed in a skiing accident several years back, just weeks before they were to be married, and he left her pregnant with his child. She was from good stock, churchgoing people with hard ideas about anticipating marriage vows. It was my nephew she was carrying. So we married, for the child's sake."

"She didn't love you?" she asked gently.

His chin lifted pugnaciously. "I'm not a lovable man," he said with a cold smile. "No, she didn't love me. She loved my brother and grieved for him the whole time we were married. Even after the baby came, she could hardly bear to let me touch her." He studied her mouth as he spoke, as if the words were coming harder by the second. "We'd taken Kip on a camping trip, up into the Rockies, and for the first time, Joyce was showing some interest in life. I'd let them ride in the trailer we were towing, against my better judgment." His eyes closed, his whole body going rigid. "The coupling came loose. They went over. . . ."

She didn't even stop to think. She slid her arms under the shepherd's coat, around him, and pressed close, holding him as hard as she could, rocking him. "I'm sorry," she whispered, her eyes closed as she gave him what little comfort she could. "I'm so sorry."

He was astonished at the gesture. His hands touched her shoulders lightly as he tried to decide what to do. The feel of her lightly clad body under his coat was disturbing him. He could feel her soft breasts pressing into him. She was clinging too hard, making his mind whirl with sensation, with soft woman smells coming up into his nostrils and making him hungry in a way he hadn't been since Joyce's death.

"It was a long time ago," he said finally. His lean hands smoothed over her hair, holding her cheek to his chest as he stopped fighting it and gave in to the feel of her against him.

"You loved her."

He hesitated. "I thought I did, yes," he agreed and wondered why he qualified it that way when he'd always assumed that it was love. Now it seemed more likely that he'd pitied Joyce, that he'd wanted to make up to her the loss of his younger brother. But now, with Maggie holding him, he wasn't sure anymore.

"And the boy."

He drew in a steadying breath. "Especially the boy," he confessed. "I missed him like hell. I still do, Maggie."

The sound of her name on his lips made her go warm and soft all over. That startled her into stiffening.

"Sorry," she said, starting to draw back.

But he held her. "No," he said quietly at her temple. "I haven't had a woman this close in years. It feels good."

His admission was shocking. She lifted her gaze to search his black, intent eyes. "Years?" she asked hesitantly, and with that one word, she was asking how experienced he really was.

He didn't want to tell her. But the way she was looking at him wasn't mocking or amused. He touched her cheek with the back of his hand. "Years," he confirmed, and that strange flush was back on his cheekbones.

Her lips parted because she wanted to know, needed to know, had to know. "Were there... many?" she whispered.

He swallowed. His eyes went over her face gently. "No," he whispered back. His jaw clenched. "Only one, if you can't live without having the whole truth," he added harshly, because he hated admitting it. In fact, he didn't know why he was even telling her.

She had to catch her breath. He looked so sophisticated, so worldly. And he was telling her blatantly that he was as inexperienced as she was. She felt a thrill go through her body that was beyond anything she'd ever felt.

He was rigid, waiting for the laughter. It didn't come. And the way she was looking at him made fires in his blood. His head lifted, and he looked down at her quietly, curiously. "No smart remarks?" he asked, challenge in the very set of his dark head.

"Oh, no," she whispered, her expression soft, adoring. "There was only my husband, you see," she replied. "And I was innocent and very young. He wasn't terribly experienced, either. We did a lot of fumbling, and I don't know if either of us was ever . . . satisfied." She buried her red face in his hard chest, feeling his heart pounding under her forehead. "I could never say that to anyone before. I could never talk to a man like this."

He felt like throwing his head back and laughing with the sheer delight of what he was learning about her. He smiled to himself, secretly, triumphantly. "And here I thought you wrote the book on city sophistication," he murmured with a soft sound that was almost a chuckle.

"Fooled you, didn't I?" she asked dreamily.

In more ways than one, but he wasn't letting his guard down that far. His hands smoothed her hair, savoring its softness. "Then come home with me, you and Blake. Until the snow's gone, at least. You'll need help bathing him, if nothing else," he persisted. "I remember how I was at his age. I'd have raised hell before I'd have let my mother give me a bath."

She laughed delightedly and lifted her head, her gray eyes sparkling, beautiful in her soft face as she looked at him. "I guess he would, too," she agreed.

"I won't hurt you," he murmured. "I don't have enough experience to seduce women. Even green little girls like you."

She smiled even wider. "Thank you, Tate," she said gently.

The sound of his name in that soft, husky tone made his heart stop beating. He searched her eyes, watching the smile falter at the intensity of the look they were exchanging. "Say my name again," he whispered.

"Tate," she obliged, her voice breathless now.

His lean hands framed her face, and holding her eyes, he bent toward her. His hard lips touched her mouth hesitantly, the mustache tickling. He was a little awkward, and his nose got in the way before he finally pressed his mouth to hers.

"God, I'm rusty," he whispered on a husky laugh. "I think I've forgotten how!"

She laughed, too, because it was delicious being with a man who was as inexperienced as she was herself. It was the sweetest kind of pleasure. She reached her arms around him and tilted her head back. "I don't mind," she whispered. "Could we try again? I'm kind of rusty, too."

He smiled, a real smile this time, and bent again. This time he wasn't awkward. His hard lips brushed hers, once, twice, and then settled, moving gently until the contact suddenly became electrically charged.

She felt the very moment when his big body stiffened, when his breath caught. She started to speak. The opening of her lips coincided with the downward movement of his, and he tasted her.

"Maggie," he groaned. He eased her back against the door, and his big body moved down, pinning her there with exquisite strength but so gently that it didn't frighten her. She felt his mouth, tasted its hard, moist crush, and her lips parted for him with a soft little cry.

She couldn't remember the last time a kiss had aroused her. Even during her brief marriage she hadn't felt this oddly weak and trembling vulnerability. Tate might be inexperienced, but there was a powerful chemistry between them if this shuddering need was any indication. She loved the hard crush of his lips, even the abrasive tickle of his mustache. And the feel of his muscular body so close was making her tingle from head to toe.

He lifted his head, and his dark eyes were black as they searched her face.

She felt drowsy, hardly capable of standing alone. "Tate," she whispered, lifting her mouth toward his blindly.

"No, honey." He moved away from her then, the endearment coming without any effort at all, although he'd never used them in his life. He held her until she got her balance back, his hands gentle but firm on her soft upper arms. "We have to stop."

She looked up at him with blank eyes that slowly darkened as she became aware of reality again. She flushed and dropped her eyes to the heavy rise and fall of his chest. "Oh, my," she said inadequately.

"You'd better get dressed," he said, fighting for reason. The bed was just behind him, and he could already feel her soft bareness against him. He shook his head to clear it. "I'll go roust Blake and help him dress."

"Thank you."

He moved her gently to one side, his hands still warm and comforting on her arms. "Maggie, are you all right?"

She forced a smile. "Just a little shaky, that's all," she said and laughed at her own weakness.

He laughed, too, because it was new to be vulnerable. And because he didn't mind if she saw that he was. She was just sweet hell to make love to. That could cause some problems, but he wasn't wasting time thinking about consequences right now.

"Me, too," he murmured, lazily studying the way her pajama top was shaking with her heartbeats. Her breasts were hard tipped. He could see their outline, and he wished for a moment that he had more experience, but since she wasn't put off by it, why should he worry?

"Stop that," she whispered, embarrassed, and crossed her arms over her chest.

He chuckled. He liked her reactions. He liked her. "Get some clothes on."

He opened the door and went out, and it was almost a minute before Maggie could even move. She tasted him on her lips, she smelled the clean scent of him on her pajama top. She and Blake were going to his house, to live with him until the snow stopped.

Until the snow stopped. She blinked. Christmas was next week, and soon she and Blake had to leave Montana. She winced. It was going to be harder than she'd expected. She didn't want to leave Montana. She didn't want to leave Tate. She turned back to her chest of drawers to get out a blouse, wondering how this sudden attachment to him had come about and how she was going to cope with it.

Tate had his own four-wheel-drive Jeep outside, and he carefully loaded Blake into it, then Maggie, along with the clothes she'd packed quickly, and they headed for his place.

Fortunately, it was a big house, and there were four bedrooms. Tate had renovated one of them and made it into an office where he did his book work, but there were three rooms with beds left. Tate had the biggest, filled with antique furniture in dark oak shades and a bed that was king-size and boasted a quilted coverlet with a Western motif.

The others were alike, pine-paneled rooms with modern furniture and trimmings in shades of brown and beige and green. Earth colors that suited him. Maggie took one room and Blake had the other.

"Who cleans the house for you?" Maggie asked as she joined him in the huge living room with its cathedral ceiling and large stone fireplace. The furniture was heavy and dark, made for comfort. There were stone ashtrays and several potted cactus plants, and even a rubber tree in one corner.

"One of my men has a compassionate wife," he murmured, smiling at her curiosity as she went around the room looking at the Indian pottery on the mantel, at the huge Hereford bull whose masculine beauty was captured in a painting above the mantel.

"Who is he...was he?" she corrected, indicating the bull.

"King's Honor," he said proudly. "He was a champion sire. Lived to be twenty years old and kept the ranch going when nothing else could. His progeny are still well-known in cattle circles."

"I wish I knew more about ranching."

"Plenty of time to learn," he said, his eyes twinkling as they met hers.

She loved to look at him. It became a habit as the day wore on. Maggie cooked supper, grilling steaks on the big expensive range in the kitchen. She made creamed potatoes and cooked some frozen beans and even made bread to go with it.

Tate was fascinated with the bread. "I didn't know women still made it," he confessed as he finished his third buttered slice.

"Mom loves to cook," Blake grinned.

"Mostly out of laziness," she confessed. "I hate eating out."

He laughed gently. "So do I." He glanced at Blake's sudden grimace. "How about something else for that leg?" he asked the boy.

"I don't really need it," Blake said.

Tate turned his chair around, staring at the boy. "I broke my leg once. Got backed up on by one of my bulls. I learned that pain hurts, and that if you don't overdo pain medication, it gets you over the bad spots. You don't have to prove anything to me," he added with a quizzical smile. "You kept your head eye to eye with a wolf. That told me all I needed to know about you."

Blake actually flushed with pleasure. "It wasn't so bad," he mumbled.

"Now how about that capsule?" Tate persisted.

Blake sighed. "OK."

Tate waved Maggie back down when she got up to get it. Instead, he rose and brought back the bottle. "Have one, then I'll teach you how to play chess. Or do you already know?"

"I can play checkers, but nobody ever taught me chess."

"No time like the present to learn," Tate said and smiled at the boy.

Maggie did the dishes and then curled up on the sofa to watch the game. Tate was patient in a way she'd never expected him to be, going over and over the moves with Blake until he understood. Her first impression of him had been that he never stopped or slowed down for anybody. But all those first impressions were undergoing change. She found that he had a dry sense of humor, that he wasn't really a bear at all and that he was rather a lonely kind of man. There was nothing in this elegant house to indicate that he was wealthy, except for the sheer size of the ranch around it. He didn't put on airs, but she imagined that he could have if it pleased him.

"It must get lonely," Maggie said absently, smoothing one of the Indian blankets that lay over the back of the sofa.

Tate looked up from the chessboard while Blake frowned in concentration over his next move. "It does," he answered her. "Especially for a woman."

She blinked, averting her eyes.

"I guess loneliness is pretty portable, though," he added, watching her. "Because I've known people who could be alone in a crowd."

"That's true enough," she conceded, trailing her finger over the design in the blanket while the fire roared like a fiery lullaby in the hearth. She was oddly sleepy. That was new, because she'd been a little jumpy at the cabin, even with Blake nearby. But here, in Tate's house, she felt safe. She smiled secretively and closed her eyes.

Tate's dark eyes wandered slowly over her face, aware of that dreamy expression on it as he tried to reconcile his misgivings with a new and staggering hunger.

Blake caught the look on the man's face before he could erase it, and he had to bite his tongue to keep from smiling. So far, so good, he thought.

Chapter Four

Blake went to sleep during a chess move, and Tate lifted him carefully, cast and all, and carried him into his room.

"Get me his pajamas," he called over his shoulder, "and I'll get him into them."

"It will take a miracle to get them over that cast," she sighed.

He smiled at her gently. "Good point. Well, get his jacket anyway, and I'll loan him a pair of my bottoms."

"I can see him now with the legs tied around his neck to hold them up," she mused.

He actually laughed. He put the boy down on the bed, hesitating as he stood watching him sleep. His dark eyes narrowed. "Nine going on ten," he said softly. "He's a hell of a boy."

Maggie caught her breath at the quiet affection in that statement and wondered if he realized how much emotion he was betraying. But after a minute he moved, frowning, and went toward his own room as if he was preoccupied.

She got Blake out of his flannel shirt and into the pajama top just as Tate came back with a pair of cotton trousers that looked new in one lean hand.

"Oh, you shouldn't let him have your newest ones...." she protested.

He gave her a faintly mocking smile. "Honey, I don't wear anything in bed. I keep a couple of pair in case of fire."

She flushed beet-red without understanding why. After marriage and a child and despite his admitted lack of experience, he could so easily reduce her to shyness.

"Sorry," she said, then added as she backed toward the door, "Well, I'll leave you to it."

He turned toward Blake, still smiling.

Minutes later, he was back. He eased down onto the sofa beside her and lit a cigarette while the fire crackled and wind occasionally whistled down the chimney.

"Does he miss not having a father?" he asked with studied carelessness.

"Sometimes I think so," she confessed. She tucked her feet under her, bare below the hem of her jeans, and folded her arms over her cotton top. It was the same shade of blue as the one Tate was wearing, and she wondered if he'd noticed that their taste in color seemed to match. "It's especially hard on him at school, although a number of the boys have divorced parents. Most of their mothers seem to have remarried or at least have boyfriends who come to the events at school."

He leaned a long arm over the back of the sofa and studied her face openly. "And there aren't any men in your life."

She smiled, not embarrassed. "I'm hopelessly old-fashioned," she explained. "I guess Blake thinks I'm a dinosaur."

"I'd bet you that he doesn't," he replied, surprising her. "He told his grandfather that he thinks you're the best mother a boy could possibly have."

Her breath caught, and she smiled. "He said that, really?"

"That's what Jeffries told me," he agreed. He took a draw of the cigarette. "I used to spend a lot of time at his place, when you and the boy were in Tucson. I heard about you until I felt as if I knew you. But I didn't, of course. Not at all. I had a totally different picture of you. I thought you probably went out a lot, but were very discreet," he added with a faint smile.

"I wouldn't know how," she sighed. "If I were involved with someone, Blake would know it instantly. I can't hide how I feel."

"Thank God," he said and meant it.

Her eyes came up, curious.

"I hate lies," he said unexpectedly. "I hate social convention and subterfuge and polite verbal warfare. I say exactly what I think, and I appreciate it when other people do. You and I got off to a rough start, but after what we said to each other back at your house, I think we're on the way to something good."

"What kind of...something good?" she asked, still a little wary of an intensity in him that she didn't quite understand.

"You tell me, Maggie," he replied quietly. He bent then and brushed his mouth very softly over hers. "Sleep tight."

He got up in one smooth motion, leaving her staring after his broad back.

"It's only eight o'clock," she said to the room at large.

"I get up before dawn. Cattle don't keep city hours," he added with a slow smile. "Turn out the lights when you're sleepy."

"OK."

She sat a little longer by the fire, spinning dreams, thinking about how it would be if they were a family, she and Tate Hollister and Blake. But they were only dreams, she reminded herself, and soon enough she'd be back at her desk at work, with only memories.

The next morning, something woke her before daylight. A sound. A movement. She got up, feeling bright eyed because she was accustomed to rising early when she had to work. She dressed in jeans and a pullover gray jersey, pausing to run a brush through her hair before she tiptoed down the hall to Blake's room and peeked in.

He was still sound asleep. She smiled, closing the door, and went into the kitchen in search of coffee. Only to find somebody else bent on the same course.

Tate was there, in his stocking feet wearing nothing but his blue jeans. She stopped dead in the doorway, her eyes helplessly drawn to a body that would have made a male centerfold look anemic. Muscles rippled under darkly tanned skin as he rose from peeking into the oven, and when he turned toward her, she wondered if it was permissible for a modern woman to swoon.

His chest was completely obscured by thick black curling hair. Muscles rippled in his big arms, down his flat stomach, and she knew there wasn't an ounce of fat anywhere on him. She'd never liked hairy men, but this one was a work of art. He didn't have tufts of hair on his arms and shoulders as some men did. No, it was all on that broad chest, thick and gleaming with faint moisture, as if he'd just come from a shower. Probably he had, because his shaggy head was a bit damp as well, his straight hair falling roguishly over his forehead.

"Good morning," he murmured, his eyes running over her face with blatant interest. "No makeup?"

"I hate the stuff," she blurted out.

He laughed. "So do I. Get some cream out of the refrigerator and I'll pour you some coffee."

"I didn't think you were so handy in the kitchen," she remarked as he took up the toast he'd been watching under the broiler and added it to a platter of thick bacon and scrambled eggs.

"Oh, Jeffries used to tell a story about one of my hands quitting because I fed him, but I'm handy enough, I guess. I was a marine, honey," he added with a quick glance as he filled two thick white mugs with coffee. "Cooking is one of the easy things you get taught."

She opened her mouth to make a comment but thought better of it. He put the coffee on the table and sat down.

"I didn't expect you to be up and about this early," he said as he filled his plate.

"I like to watch the sun come up," she confessed. "It's magic in Tucson, when dawn hits the Santa Catalina mountains. They change color. Sometimes they're red, sometimes black, then they turn pink and rust . . . they haunt me."

"I've seen my own mountains change, but from blue to purple," he told her. "And dead white in winter. Have some eggs. You need feeding up."

"I never gain weight," she confessed as she reached for a piece of toast to go with her slice of bacon. She watched as he dumped eggs on her plate. "That's too much," she told him.

"If you're going to live on a ranch, you have to keep up your strength. Blake will tell you that." He was through his eggs already and working on homemade jam and toast.

"I won't be out pitching hay and fixing fences and checking on cattle," she reminded him.

"What did you plan to do?" he asked curiously.

"I thought I'd clean the house, if you don't mind— not that it needs it, but the beds will have to be made." She dropped her gaze. The sight of his bare chest at close range was making her weak in the knees. "I wouldn't want to interfere with your cleaning lady, of course."

"You won't interfere. Do whatever you like. Within reason, of course. I get funny about lace on my undershirts."

"Do you wear one?" she blurted out, and blushed as she realized how intimate the question sounded.

He was watching the way her eyes glanced off his chest, and she couldn't know how much a man her shy appreciation made him feel. His dark eyes narrowed on her face. "No, I don't," he answered the question. He finished his toast and swallowed the rest of his coffee. "Want a second cup?"

"Yes. I'll get it." She got up, but as she went past him, his lean hand shot out and caught her wrist.

"No, you won't," he murmured dryly, and jerked.

She fell across his lap, gasping, one slender hand coming into sudden, shocking contact with all that bare chest. She couldn't even protest. Her gaze fell to where her hand was half-buried. She didn't want him to see how vulnerable she was, but it took too much work to try and hide her blatant interest.

He pressed her hand flat against him, looking at the small ovals of her nails without polish. She had nice hands, very slender and graceful. "Stop hiding from me." He tilted her face to his so that he could see all the doubts and nervousness. His black eyes were kind for all the darkness growing in them. "This is as new for me as it is for you, so don't think I'm going to make fun of the way you're looking at me. I'd be staring just as hard at you if your shirt was off."

Her lips parted. "Really?"

"Really." He moved her hand against the thick hair and hard, warm muscle beneath it, watching the movement, feeling its instant effect on him. He laughed, the sound deep and low and pleasant in the early morning stillness. He looked up to see an arrested fascination in her eyes. "I thought I was immune. Feel." He put her hand over his heart and let her feel its hard, heavy beat.

"I guess none of us are...immune, that is," she whispered.

"Is yours beating that hard?" he asked softly and, still holding her gaze, his lean hand pressed just under the soft breast. But his other arm came up at the same time, arching her, and he eased her down into the crook of it while his long fingers spread. The tips of them just touched the soft underswell of her breast, bare under the jersey, and she couldn't breathe. She began to tremble and her eyes darkened to old silver, staring up into his black ones.

"Tate," she whispered huskily, her breath catching.

"I suppose there are rules about this sort of thing," he said tautly, holding her eyes as his fingertips traced the swell of her breast. "Back in the Dark Ages when I was a boy, nice girls would slap a man for what I'm trying to do to you."

"I'm a widow, not a girl," she breathed shakily. "And I...like...what you're doing to me."

"You aren't supposed to tell me that, Maggie," he whispered as his head bent toward her. He brushed his lips over hers once, twice, and then they settled on her mouth. His hand searched for the hem of the jersey, found it and went up until it found a warm, soft mound with a hard tip that arched into his palm even as she shuddered with rapt sensation.

She moaned under his mouth. He tasted her, felt her hunger, drowned in her yielding softness.

When she tensed again, without taking his mouth from hers, he pushed the jersey out of the way and pulled her against his bare chest. She tensed, gasping as her breasts melted into the thick hair and warm muscle of him. His head lifted, because he wanted to see her face.

His dark eyes narrowed. She looked...wild. Abandoned. Her lips were swollen, her eyes half-closed, misty and faintly savage all at once. She was flushed and her body arched toward his.

His eyes went down to her breasts, and he looked at the contrasts between what he could see of her pink and mauve flesh and his hair-matted darkly tanned chest. His arm tightened, but he lifted a little away, because it had been years since he'd seen a woman without clothes, and he wanted to look at Maggie's soft breasts.

She saw him visibly start at his first real sight of her that way. His face hardened, his eyes began to glitter. He frowned slightly, looking intently at her body. As if fascinated, one lean, dark-fingered hand came up to touch the round contour with its blatant hardness, and she gasped at that tender tracing because the excitement she was feeling was so intense.

His black eyes moved back up to hers. "You fascinate me," he whispered tautly. "All of you. Your body, your heart, your mind. I've always thought of women in physical terms until now. But, I touch you and I wonder..."

"Wonder what?" she asked in a soft whisper, because it was almost reverent with him.

"I wonder how it would be if I gave you a child," he whispered, his tone full of awe.

She stopped breathing. His words held that kind of impact. Her eyes searched his face, and she lifted her hand to touch his mouth, to trace the thick mustache, the hard cheek, the thick brows. His eyes closed and he sat quietly and a little tensely while her soft hand went over him, learning the contours of his face.

She arched then and touched her mouth with aching tenderness to his. Her fingers found his, pressing them down over the softly mounded flesh, holding his palm there while her mouth made slow, sweet love to his.

"You're killing me," he whispered on a tortured laugh.

"You aren't doing my metabolism much good, either," she whispered at his lips. She was sitting up on his lap, with both hands on his chest, and her eyes were full of emotion. Their color was soft, like gray doves.

He took a deep breath and forced himself to pull her jersey down, smoothing it around her waist. "I've got to go to work," he groaned. "My God, I hope I can pitch hay bent over double."

He was laughing, though, and her eyes blazed with triumph, with delighted knowledge on her part in his downfall. She smiled at him, and her hands smoothed back his thick dark hair, lingering at his temples.

"What would you like for lunch?" she asked.

"Anything," he replied. "As long as I get to look at you while I eat it."

"Oh, Tate." She put her mouth over his and clung to him, feeling him move, feeling his lean hand gather her hips suddenly against his.

He felt her tauten. His head lifted and he looked into her wide, frightened gray eyes. "I won't hurt you, Maggie," he whispered. "I just want you to know how

much a man I am with you. It isn't a threat. It's..."
He paused. "I don't know. Pride, I think," he decided finally, and it was in his eyes, in his whole look.

She met his level gaze and the fear was gone, all at once. She relaxed into him, forcing her taut muscles to give, forcing her body to trust him. "It's difficult," she said softly. "I've spent years holding back."

"I understand." He kissed her closed eyelids and then he let her go, helping her back onto her feet as he rose and towered over her. "I didn't bring you here to seduce you," he added, framing her face in his warm, strong hands. "There's nothing to be afraid of."

"But I am afraid," she whispered, frowning as she looked up at him. "Tate, I... We mustn't..."

He put a long finger against her soft lips. "I have to go." He brushed his hard mouth over her forehead, and the mustache tickled. "Let's live one day at a time. OK?"

She forced herself not to panic. "OK," she agreed.

He smiled. He seemed to do a lot of that lately, she thought, watching him go down the hall to his bedroom. But, then, so did she.

The days that followed were magic. Tate didn't touch her again, although she could see the banked-down fire in his eyes when he looked at her; she could read the hunger there. He spent time with Blake at night when he wasn't working, talking cattle and marketing, things that went right over Maggie's head, but that Blake seemed to understand and really enjoy. And when Tate loaned him his *Stockman's Handbook* to study, the boy was over the moon.

"It's got a whole section on feedlot management," Blake said enthusiastically.

"We could use a feedlot around here. I just never seem to get time to look into the possibilities," Tate said, leaning back on the sofa with a cup of black coffee and smoking a cigarette. "But it's interesting all the same to see how they're operated. There's more to it than just grouping numbers of cattle together and feeding them twice a day."

"This is interesting, about the danger of explosive gases," Blake murmured.

Maggie looked up from her *Ranch* magazine, where she was going over a recipe for a beef casserole. "Gases?"

Blake went into a long and nauseating explanation of how the unvented waste from livestock could create explosive and toxic gases, while Tate watched, faintly amused at her wide-eyed disgust.

"Son, I don't think your mother's in raptures over the gory details," he murmured. "She might find some tips on range management a little easier to take."

"Right," Blake agreed readily, flushed because his idol had actually called him "son." He looked at Tate with more emotion than he realized, so hungry for a father of his own that he was as open as a book.

Tate, watching that expression unfold, felt a wild stirring inside himself. A protective stirring, just as he had the morning he'd shot at the wolf when it threatened Blake. The boy and the woman were getting to him, growing on him, taking him over. Once, he'd have drawn back in anger from that kind of affection. But now...

He looked at Maggie, his eyes quiet and tender on her down-bent dark head as she read her magazine. She and Blake were already part of his life; it was as natural as breathing. He looked forward to coming home at lunch, at night. He looked forward to every new day. That was when it dawned on him that Christmas was five days away and they'd be going back to Arizona soon afterwards. He felt sick all over.

To ward off thought of the future without them, he got to his feet. "What are we going to do about a tree?" he asked suddenly.

They both stared at him.

"Well, we have to have a tree," he explained. "It's going to be Christmas in five days."

Maggie felt the same sickness he'd just experienced at the thought of what came after the holiday, but she forced herself to smile. "What are we going to put on it?" she asked. "Do you have any decorations?"

"We could put one of my hats on top, I guess," he mused, "and whip a rope around it for a garland."

"We could put it in one of your boots," Blake chuckled and got a black glare for his pains.

"Suppose we make decorations?" Maggie pondered. "I can bake cookies in different shapes to go around it, and do you have some popcorn and thread?" Tate nodded and she grinned. "We can make garlands of popcorn. But what about Christmas dinner? Tate, can you get a ham and a turkey?"

"There are three hams in the deep freeze," Tate replied. "But a turkey..." He frowned. "I guess I could get one from Jane Clyde, over the mountain."

"Is it far?" Maggie asked.

"Just an hour's drive or so."

She thought of him on that winding road, of how dangerous it was in snow and ice. "We don't need a turkey," she said. "Really, I hate turkey. And so does Blake," she added, daring her son to argue.

But he was quick, was Blake. He'd already followed her reasoning and was agreeing with enthusiasm that turkeys were the curse of civilization.

Tate didn't say anything else about going over the mountain to get a bird. But he smiled to himself when he left the room. They weren't fooling anybody—he saw right through them.

For the next few days, Maggie and Blake worked on decorations and made presents. Since the nearest store was down the mountain, they decided to make do with what they'd brought with them from Tucson. Maggie had Tate run her back to the cabin to check on everything, and she dug out the shopping bags full of things she'd brought with her from the city for Christmas.

"More decorations," she murmured, tossing out tinsel and gently laying a box of colored balls on the sofa. "And this is what Blake especially wanted for Christmas." She showed him a computer game, one of the very expensive ones with graphics and three diskettes.

He pursed his lips. "Very nice. I have a PC compatible, but I hadn't realized that Blake had an interest in computers."

"You have a computer?" she asked with vivid curiosity because she was thinking up a present for Tate, since he was the one person she hadn't foreseen a need to buy one for.

"Sure. Over 600 kilobytes of storage space, double disk drive, with a modem and a daisy wheel printer." He smiled at her fascination. "I keep my herd records on computer these days. It beats the hell out of having to handwrite every entry."

"Do you have a spreadsheet program?" she fished.

"I do, indeed," he said and named it. It was one of the more expensive ones, so that program was out.

"What I don't have," he sighed, studying Blake's disk, "is a good word processing program. I could use one of those to write letters with." He glanced at her, noticing her rapt expression, and he grinned again. He had two word processors, but he wasn't about to tell her. He'd rush home and hide those disks, fast!

"My, my, they do come in handy, don't they?" she mused and quickly hid the one she'd bought for Blake. Blake could wait another Christmas for a word processing program; he wasn't getting this one.

They loaded her packages in the car after she'd taken time to wrap them. "Tate, I never thought," she said as they got into the jeep, "is there anyone you spend Christmas with? Your family?"

"My parents are long dead, Maggie," he said quietly. "I have no one."

"I'm sorry, I didn't mean to pry."

He took her slender hand in his and pressed his mouth to the palm. "You and I aren't going to have any secrets from each other," he said tenderly. "I don't mind telling you anything you want to know."

He let go of her hand and started the Jeep, and she thought about what he'd said all the way home.

* * *

Home. It felt like home. She finished the last of the icing on the Japanese fruitcake she'd made, with its one mince layer and two white layers and exotic candied fruit icing with coconut all over it. It was like the cake her mother had always made back home. She wondered if she could ask Tate later about phoning her youngest brother Michael on Christmas Eve and charging the bill to her phone in Tucson. Oddly enough, she hadn't missed having a telephone at the cabin, but she knew Tate had one because she'd heard him talking on it occasionally. Michael still lived in Tennessee, and he kept in touch with the rest of the family. Maggie wanted to know how Jack and Sam and their families were, and Michael was always good about passing messages along. Dear Michael, with his hair as dark as her own and eyes almost as gray as hers.

"What are you dreaming about?" Tate asked, reaching past her to refill his coffee cup while he and Blake took a short break from one of the old computer games Maggie had brought over.

"About Michael," she said without thinking and looked up to see a flash of lightning in Tate's black eyes.

"Who's Michael?" he asked tersely.

"Oh, I like that," she said softly and smiled up at him. "I like the way you sound when you think there's another man in my life. But there isn't, you know. Michael is my younger brother. He's just twenty-two, and he looks like me, except in places."

He mellowed. His lean fingers brushed back her thick hair. "Does he?" He bent, nuzzling her cheek with his. "I'm getting possessive. Does it bother you?"

"Look at another woman and you'll see how much it bothers me."

He lifted his head, searching her eyes quietly. "I see what you mean," he mused.

"What?"

He rubbed his nose against hers. "I like it, too."

His breath was on her mouth. "Like what?"

"Having you get possessive. Open your mouth."

She did and his brushed against it, open, too. He bit at her lip, his mustache abrasive, his mouth hard. He grasped the back of her neck and pulled her closer, crushing her mouth under the warm pressure of his.

"Would you bring me a cola, Mr. Hollister?" Blake called suddenly from the office, shocking them apart.

Maggie could hardly breathe. Tate seemed to be having a bit of a problem in that direction himself. He stood up, blinking. "A what?" he called.

"A soda."

"Sure." He shook his head, whistling through his teeth as he got one out of the refrigerator. "Heady stuff."

"What is, cola?" she murmured dryly, although her heart was still pounding.

"You," he whispered and kissed her again, softly, as he went past her to the study.

She leaned against the counter, watching his broad back disappear into the room with the computer, and she thought dreamily how sweet it would be if they were married and she never had to go back to Tucson.

But despite their closeness and the way Tate was with them, she had to remember that she was only a guest and in less than five days she and Blake would be in Tucson and this would only be a memory.

Tears stung her eyes as she finished icing the cake. Only a memory, perhaps, but one that would haunt her the rest of her life. The thought of being away from Tate now was worse than the threat of death. And whatever he felt, he was keeping his own counsel. He wanted her, that she knew. But there was a chasm between wanting and loving, and one was nothing without the other.

Chapter Five

Getting Blake to go to bed on Christmas Eve was like trying to put a pair of pants on an eel, Maggie thought as she watched him make his fourth reappearance.

"Mr. Hollister, is there or isn't there a Santa Claus?" he asked Tate.

Maggie stared blankly at Tate, who was struggling valiantly not to give the show away.

"Santa Claus is like a spirit, Blake," he finally told the boy as he sipped his coffee on the sofa. "So in a sense, yes, he exists."

"But he doesn't come down fireplaces?"

"I didn't say that," Tate replied.

Blake bit his lower lip, leaning heavily on the crutch Tate had loaned him. "But there's a fire in it," he groaned.

"Fire," Tate improvised, "can't possibly hurt a Christmas spirit like old Santa. He can get right through it to the stockings."

"Are you sure?" Blake asked worriedly.

Tate put his hand over his heart. "Blake, would I lie to you?" he asked.

Maggie had to bite her tongue almost through to keep from laughing at the expression on Tate's face. But Blake let out a pent-up sigh and grinned.

"OK," he said. "I just wanted to be sure. Good night. See you early in the morning!"

"You, too, darling," Maggie smiled, kissing his forehead gently. "Sleep well."

"Ha, ha," he muttered, glancing ruefully at the huge pine with its homemade decorations in the corner by the window. All lit with colorful lights and smelling of the whole outdoors, it had turned out to be a better tree than anyone had expected. But the crowning touch was some soap flakes that Maggie had found in the kitchen cabinet. She'd mixed them with water and made "snow" to go on the branches. The finished product was a dream of a Christmas tree, right down to the paper snowflakes that Blake had cut out—something he'd learned to do in art class in school.

Maggie sighed as she looked at the tree. "Isn't it lovely?" she asked absently.

"Not half as lovely as you are," Tate remarked quietly, his dark eyes possessive on her body in its sleek silver dress, a long camisole of sequins and spangles that had impressed her with its holiday spirit. With her dark hair short and curled forward, she looked like one of the twenties flappers.

"I'm glad you like it," she curtsied for him with her coffee cup held tightly in one hand. Like him, she didn't drink—rarely even a glass of wine. They were celebrating Christmas with black coffee, despite her dress and his suit slacks, white shirt and navy blazer.

He turned off the top light, leaving the winking, blinking colorful lights of the tree to brighten the room. His arms slid around her waist as they looked

at the paper angel Blake had made for the tip-top.
"I'm sorry we couldn't get you up there," he mused.
"You'd make a pretty angel."

"I'd rather be just a woman," she said, turning.
Her eyes ran over his face quietly although her heart
was beating her to death. It had been forever since that
morning when he'd made such sweet love to her in the
kitchen. And she wanted that, and more, tonight. Her
whole body ached for him.

He touched her throat with the very tip of his fore-
finger, watching the pulse throb there, watching her
lips part. She was his. She didn't even have to tell him.
He could see it in her eyes, in her face, in the body that
leaned toward his in the semibright darkness.

He took a step forward, so that he was against her,
and his head bent to hers. His mouth brushed her open
one, feeling with shock the sudden darting movement
of her tongue against his upper lip.

He caught his breath and her eyes opened lazily,
looking at him.

"It...it's something I learned when I was in my
teens," she faltered.

"It's damned arousing, do you know that?" he
asked quietly. "Having Blake in the house wouldn't
even slow me down, Maggie, so don't look for miracles if you start something tonight."

He made it sound as if she was making him a proposition. Well, she was, but he didn't have to make her
feel cheap for it. She'd taken certain things about their
relationship for granted, but perhaps she'd presumed
too far. She'd wanted a memory of him, something
warm and private, just for the two of them. A Christ-

mas memory that she could take back to the desert with her to last all the long, lonely years that she was going to spend grieving for him.

Her head bent. Her hands clenched around her coffee cup. "I'm sorry," she whispered.

His breath caught. He hadn't expected her reaction. He hadn't meant to shame her, for heaven's sake. He'd just been hesitant to let things get out of hand before he could get up his nerve to ask her if she might consider staying at the ranch—she and Blake. He started to speak when a thunderous knocking at the front door broke the spell.

He jerked it open and a man was standing there, a very old one in a ragged hat. "Sorry to bother you, boss, but Katie Bess is due." He grinned. "I knew you'd want to be there."

"Yes. I do. Thanks, Baldy."

He closed the door and turned. "Katie Bess is one of my Shetland sheepdogs," he explained. "We use them to help us herd cattle. Katie Bess is our newest, and she and her pups are purebred."

"Christmas babies," Maggie said with a smile, trying to live down her humiliation. "Can I come, too?"

"Sure. But not in that," he said with a faint grin.

"I'll hurry and change."

"What's going on?" Blake called as they went past his door.

"Never mind." Maggie peeked in his door and told him, "Go back to sleep. Santa may come while we're outside, but only if he thinks you're snoring."

"I am, I am!" he promised, snoring loudly.

Maggie laughed as she closed the door. She got into her red flannel shirt and a pair of jeans, thick socks and boots, grabbed her parka and rushed out into the hall. Tate was already ahead of her, his boots making loud thuds as he went toward the hall closet and jerked out his shepherd's coat and hat.

She followed him to the stable where the mother sheepdog, who resembled a small collie with her fluffy tan and white fur, was lying in a clean stall. There were already three tiny furry bodies nuzzling close as the puppies nursed. And even as they watched, a fourth and fifth were born. Tate and Baldy spoke encouragingly to the dog, of which they were both obviously fond, and commented glowingly on the pups. They were like patchwork in color, beige and brown and white and brown and tan and white, and Maggie would have loved to pick them up and cuddle them. But they were too tiny just yet, and she satisfied herself with watching, adoring the tiny things with her eyes.

When she was a child, her parents had always kept her away from the animals when they were about to give birth. Far from thinking it would be an interesting experience for her, they were horrified at the thought that it might frighten her. But this wasn't a frightening experience; it was a humbling one.

The dog bent, licking the soft little coats. Her liquid brown eyes were as tender as a human mother's, her tired body shivering a little in reaction.

"I'll get some milk for her," Baldy said, moving away.

Tate's lean hand found Maggie's in the semidarkness under the central hanging light bulb. "She's been sick," he explained, "and we were afraid she might need help. But as you can see, she was up to it. That's a fine litter, Katie Bess," he said gently to the dog, who wagged her tail and looked up at him as if she loved him. "Good girl."

Baldy came back with milk and some fresh meat. "I'll take care of her now, boss. Looks like more snow coming, but Merry Christmas anyway."

"Merry Christmas, Baldy," Tate chuckled. "I guess we've both got our presents tonight."

"Guess we have, although yours looks a mite prettier than mine, but just a mite, mind," the old man said with a smothered chuckle.

Tate didn't seem to take offense. He wished the old man a good night, and he and Maggie went back toward the house.

The snow was coming down softly, but the wind was calm. They could see for miles in the white landscape, the snow lighting the way as surely as a lamp. Tate stopped to light a cigarette and slid his arm around Maggie's shoulders as they walked.

"Was it hard for you, when Blake was born?" he asked unexpectedly.

She looked up at him. "You mean, was it hard physically?" He nodded, and she let her eyes slide back to the house, silhouetted against the snow and the mountains and the dark sky. "I guess it was. But it's his face I remember, not the pain. Life is like that, isn't it? We may remember the cut, but it's the kiss that came afterward that stays in the memory."

"Profound thoughts on a Christmas Eve," he murmured.

"Yes. It's a profound night." She sighed, feeling his strength near her, dwarfing her, supporting her. "A night for miracles."

"I haven't celebrated Christmas since the accident," he said. "I haven't cared about much. But you and Blake have made the color come back into the world for me," he added, looking down at her. "You've brought me out of the past, out of the shadows. I think I'd forgotten how to smile until you came along."

She smiled up at him, but her heart felt heavy. Was that a way of saying goodbye and thanks for the hand? Or was it more? She was afraid to ask him for anything.

"I'm glad you've remembered how again," she said, forcing her eyes back to the path.

"About what I said in there," he murmured, nodding toward the house. He hesitated. His dark eyes cut down to hers. "I didn't mean to embarrass you. Maggie, if you want me, all you have to do is say so."

The blatant shock of the words stunned her. She couldn't even answer him for a few seconds. Yes, she did want him all right. But he made it sound matter-of-fact, like offering a thirsty traveler a drink of water. She flushed violently.

"I...I'm sleepy," she faltered. "I'd better get some rest so that I can cope with dinner tomorrow. Thanks for letting me see the pups!"

She practically ran up onto the porch and through the quiet house to her room, tears glistening in her eyes. She couldn't look at Tate, and that was a shame, because the look on his face would have told her everything she needed to know.

After she'd put on her pajamas, the same blue ones she'd worn at the cabin, she paced the floor with the lights off. She paused at the window, looking out into the snowy darkness with eyes that didn't see. Christmas was tomorrow. Then, in two days, they'd be gone.

She closed her eyes on a groan and got into bed. She had to forget. No, she had to make plans. She'd been coasting, loving Tate, getting to know him. But there was no future in it, and she'd been making dreams, not plans. Now she had to decide. Did she keep the ranch? Did she send Blake back to school? Did she go back to Tucson?

She worried the question for hours. Finally, in desperation, she got out of bed. Surely Tate would be asleep by now, and she needed a cup of coffee and an aspirin for the headache she'd given herself. Hopefully she wouldn't run headlong into Santa Claus out there, she mused.

But when she went into the dark kitchen and collided with a warm shape, she let out a faint gasp until she saw Tate's face silhouetted in the light from the Christmas tree.

"What are you doing up?" she faltered.

He let his dark eyes run slowly over her body in the pajamas, and he smiled because she was so obviously embarrassed at not having on a robe.

"I'm about to make coffee," he mused. "But now that you're up, you can do it while I put some clothes on."

That was when she realized that he didn't have anything on. She kept her eyes on his face with wide-eyed apprehension that tore a deep laugh from his throat.

"My God, is it that much of a shock?" he whispered wickedly.

"I've never even seen a naked man!" she screeched, and it was true because she'd never looked at her husband, not once.

His eyebrows arched in the faint light from the tree. "And you were married? Well, lady, you're overdue."

"No, I'm not." She closed her eyes tight, and he laughed as he turned back down the hall.

"All right, coward."

But she peeked. Just as he went into his room, the streaming light from it silhouetted him and she got an eyeful. He was the most magnificent man she'd ever seen, with or without clothes. She turned into the kitchen feeling poleaxed. He could have been a centerfold, all right, she thought dazedly.

He was back in less than five minutes, but only clad in his jeans. His feet were bare, like hers, and so was the rest of him.

"I thought you'd gone to sleep," she murmured. She plugged in the percolator, having already filled it with water and coffee and laid out cups and saucers and cream.

"I couldn't sleep," he said quietly. "I wanted you too badly."

Her eyes lifted. "But..."

He shrugged his broad shoulders. His lean hand touched her cheek. "I know. I frightened you off.

Maybe I meant to." He sighed heavily. "I'm still in the learning stages about seduction."

"I thought you didn't want me."

"I finally realized that," he said on a soft laugh.

She managed a tight smile and let her eyes fall to his chest, but the bare expanse of it disturbed her, so she averted her gaze to the tree.

"I forgot to call Michael," she mentioned.

"Is it too late?"

"The time zones are a couple of hours apart," she recalled, "and it's later on the East Coast. I guess he's asleep. It's just as well, anyway. I haven't quite decided what I'm going to do."

He caught her waist and leaned back against the kitchen counter, bringing her lazily against him. "Decided to do about what?"

"About the ranch. And Blake." She stared at his chin. "And me."

"Well, I can't see any real problem, honey," he said carelessly. "I want to buy the ranch, so that gets it out of the way. And Blake doesn't want to go to military school; he wants to live here and learn the cattle business. That takes care of him. Which only leaves you and me."

She swallowed. Her heart was going wild. She looked up hesitantly, her eyes faintly pleading. "You and me?"

"Mmm-hmm." He bent, brushing her nose with his. He smiled softly. "And that means," he whispered at her lips, "that you're not going anywhere until I say so, pretty girl."

"But I can't...my job...responsibilities..." she protested weakly, the words muffled by his lips.

"Hush," he chuckled, and his mouth opened lazily, taking her lips with it. She made a faint sound, but he held her close until she gave in, and then he unbuttoned her pajama jacket.

"Tate!" she protested against his hungry mouth.

"God, you're soft," he whispered as his hands tenderly took the soft weight of her breasts. He eased the fabric away from them and pulled her against him, holding her there, drawing her lazily from side to side so that the thick hair on his chest made delicious patterns on her softness, so that the hunger got worse by the second and she began to make noises that he liked.

Her nails bit into his shoulders and she clung, her mouth as eager as his.

His lean hands slid down to her hips and pulled them gently against his thighs, pressing her to him so that she could feel how much he wanted her. "I go crazy when I get close to you," he said huskily. "Eventually I'll give in to it, and so will you. We have to do something about it."

Her hands slid over his broad chest, savoring the feel of it, adoring him. "Yes."

He bit at her mouth. "When?"

Her eyes opened. "What?"

"When do you want to get married?" he asked simply, his black eyes soft, tender.

She stared at him blankly. "You...you want to marry me?" she stumbled.

"Of course I want to marry you." His shoulders lifted and fell and his mustache twitched. "Can you see us living in sin with Blake around?" he chuckled.

"But, marriage," she said quietly. Her pale eyes searched his dark ones. "You haven't wanted anyone around you."

"Yes, that's true," he said honestly. "But you know how it's been for the past week. You have opened doors for me." His hands slid up her bare back and down again, smoothing her breasts against him, shuddering a little with the sweet pleasure of it. "Maggie, I've learned that I can't live in the past. And I don't want to, not anymore. I want a family. I want you. And Blake. I don't want to spend the rest of my life alone, and I don't think you want to, either." His dark eyes narrowed. "Or have I read it wrong? Is it just a physical thing with you?"

"I want you like crazy," she admitted without embarrassment. "But it isn't just a physical thing. I love being with you. I feel safe and happy." She stared down at his chest, where her fingers were buried. "I . . ."

"Don't stop now, for God's sake," he whispered huskily. "Say it."

She looked up, flushing. "You didn't."

"I won't—not until you do," he said. "What's the matter, city girl, balking at the last fence?"

Her chin shot forward and she glared at his smug expression. "Well, you know already, don't you?" she challenged.

"Of course I know," he said with barely concealed impatience. "You were trying to seduce me before we went to see the pups, weren't you? That isn't the kind of thing a virtuous woman does unless she's pretty stuck on a man."

Her blush got worse. "Maybe I just got hot and bothered," she muttered.

"Fat chance. Say it." He nibbled at her mouth and his hands slid up her sides, smoothing blatantly over her breasts and making her moan. "Say it, woman, for God's sake!"

"I love you," she murmured. "I love you, you horrible, wonderful man—" His hard lips cut her off, and her mouth was taken, possessed, absorbed, the second the last word was dying on the air, his hands strong and warm and tender on her soft breasts as he made them burn with pleasure.

He bent, lifting her, his big body shuddering with unconcealed hunger. "It's been years," he whispered roughly, "and I want you like hell. But I'll be gentle with you."

Her arms tightened around his neck and she buried her face in his throat, trembling. "I don't care if you aren't," she whispered. "I love you so much. I want you just the way you are, Tate."

He groaned, laughing, as he carried her down the long hall. "My God, this is going to be sweet," he whispered.

She flushed, laughing. "I go all giddy and wild when you touch me."

"Just remember that Blake's a light sleeper," he whispered.

She nibbled at his jaw as he carried her, savoring the feel of his broad, warm chest, the clean scent of his body. He was going to be her lover, and she could hardly wait. This was like nothing she'd ever experienced, not even in the excitement of her first marriage. This was the promise of heaven and only the beginning of a long, achingly sweet relationship....

"Santa Claus!"

They'd just passed Blake's room and were at the door of Tate's when the sleepy young voice froze them in place. If Tate hadn't been quite so hungry, the look on his face would have been comical as he swung around with Maggie close in his arms to see Blake ambling slowly toward the living room with his crutch under his arm and cast bumping the floor.

"Santa Claus!" Blake called again.

"Damn," Tate whispered huskily. "He thinks he heard Saint Nick."

"Thank God," Maggie whispered back, frantically buttoning buttons while her face blazed with embarrassment.

He put her down, smiling faintly at her panic. "Calm down," he said gently. "Nothing happened."

"By the skin of our teeth," she moaned. She looked up at him and her heart stopped. "Oh, I love you," she breathed huskily. "And if it had happened, I wouldn't be sorry."

"I wonder," he mused. He bent and brushed his mouth gently over hers. "I lost my head, but I think it might be a good idea if we do it by the book. For Blake's sake."

She smiled dreamily. "That sounds nice. Too bad your heart's giving the show away," she added, pressing her hand over its hard, heavy beat.

"My body and my mind don't always agree," he confessed, but he was smiling, too.

Lights went on in the living room. "Wow!" came a hearty exclamation from a young voice. "Mom! Mr. Hollister! Wake up! Santa's been here!"

"Make that Mom and Dad, Blake," Tate called down the hall.

There was a short, shocked pause, a gasp and then a yell that could have awakened the dead.

"I think he's pleased," Maggie murmured.

"Do tell," Tate said, grinning. "I am, too. Well, we might as well go and open our presents, since we aren't going to give each other our best one just yet."

"There'll be time for that," she replied.

His dark eyes searched her gray ones. "All the time in the world," he agreed. "But we get married first."

"Yes, Mr. Hollister," she whispered.

Blake was already through his first two packages when they joined him, his eyes bright with love as he showed Tate and Maggie his new copy of the *Stockman's Handbook* and the software for his computer.

"But my best present," he told them, "is my new dad."

Tate ruffled his hair affectionately. "I hope it was worth that broken leg," he murmured dryly.

Blake flushed. "You knew?"

"I used to be a boy myself," Tate chuckled. "Yes, I knew."

"But how?" Maggie asked gently.

He gave her a rueful glance. "Well, you see, honey, while he was trying to get himself lost, I was busy sabotaging your generator so you'd have to spend Christmas week with me.''

"Tate!" she gasped.

He smiled at Blake, who was laughing openly. "A man gets lonely. Maybe old Scrooge had a humbug attitude toward Christmas, but I wanted a tree and someone to help me enjoy it." He shrugged. "Hard to find company up here in the mountains, unless you trap it."

Maggie hugged him on one side, and Blake did on the other. He held them both gently, fighting the sting of moisture in his dark eyes. Christmas had brought him gifts he'd never imagined, and he had them in his arms.

A week later, Blake was in school in Deer Lodge, crutches and all, and Maggie and Tate were just home from the justice of the peace's office. They'd just been married, with Blake as a witness and had dropped him off at school on their way back to the ranch. Maggie and Tate were alone for the first time, and she was afraid.

It was harder than Maggie had realized, the newness of belonging to a man after so many years of being alone. She felt like a beet when she glanced at her husband and hated her own feelings of inadequacy and nervousness.

He took her gently by the waist and looked down into her soft, frightened eyes. "Listen," he said gently, "I'm just as nervous as you are. Probably more, because I've got to set the pace. So just relax, Mrs.

Hollister, and we'll kiss each other stupid and see where it gets us. Okay?''

She lifted her face to his, smiling shyly, and closed her eyes as his mouth settled gently on hers.

As he'd thought, once she relaxed and stopped being shy with him, everything fell into place. Minutes later, they were on his king-size bed, fighting the clothes that separated them until nothing did, not even the faint chill of the air.

"Slowly," he whispered, stilling her movements, holding her. "Slowly, honey. Yes. Yes, like that," he murmured against her mouth as she shifted, letting him guide her. His lean hands caught her hips and held them as he moved. His mouth became demanding then, his hands insistent. He paused, breathing roughly, and felt her trembling. Then he moved again and it was easy. So easy. So sweet.

She clung to him, feeling his movements, feeling him breathe, feeling the wildness of his heartbeat over her breasts as his body slowly merged with hers. She'd been afraid, but there was nothing to be afraid of. He was her husband and she loved him, and this was the most beautiful expression of love that she'd ever dreamed of.

Her eyes closed as he shifted again and she opened her mouth against his throat as she heard him whispering, heard the words, burned with the passion in them. She arched, trembling, clinging, and heard his breath catch even as her body began to echo the sweet rhythm of his. And all at once they were soul to soul, as close as flesh could get to flesh. One.

She could barely breathe at all, and she was still trembling in the aftermath when she felt his eyes on her face. She opened her eyes, looking up, fascinated, into the black tenderness of his gaze.

"I love you," he whispered huskily.

"I love you, too." She reached up, clinging to him, shuddering in completion. "Tate, it was...it was never..."

"Never like this," he finished for her. He nuzzled her cheek with his. "I know." He wrapped her close, savoring her soft warmth in his arms. "You know," he whispered, "if we do this enough, you might get pregnant."

She smiled into his throat. "I've heard it said that a ranch needs lots of sons."

"Well, we've got lots of time," he whispered, lifting his head. "And I'd like to give you children, Maggie," he said, bending. "I'll love you all my life. All the way to the grave. Good times, bad times, all the times we share. You're my world."

"Oh, Tate, you're my world, too," she whispered brokenly, burying her face against him.

"Come here," he whispered. "Show me."

She tried to answer him, but there was so much emotion in her throat she couldn't speak for it. Two lost, lonely people had found a miracle this Christmas. And as she pressed against him, she managed to smile through tears of exquisite joy, her heart brimming over as she thought of all the Christmases yet to come that she and Blake would share with him— Christmases bright with laughter and filled with love.

* * * * *